5

NEW
COUNTDOWN

Second Edition

OXFORD
UNIVERSITY PRESS

OXFORD
UNIVERSITY PRESS

Great Clarendon Street, Oxford OX2 6DP

Oxford University Press is a department of the University of Oxford.
It furthers the University's objective of excellence in research, scholarship,
and education by publishing worldwide in

Oxford New York

Auckland Cape Town Dar es Salaam Hong Kong Karachi Kuala Lumpur
Madrid Melbourne Mexico City Nairobi New Delhi Shanghai Taipei Toronto

With offices in
Argentina Austria Brazil Chile Czech Republic France Greece
Guatemala Hungary Italy Japan Poland Portugal Singapore
South Korea Switzerland Turkey Ukraine Vietnam

This book is a revised edition of *Primary Mathematics for India*
by L.W. Downes, D. Paling, and Shamlu Dudeja.

The author would like to extend her gratitude to Anahita Choksey of Cathedral School, Bombay
for help in putting together the revised edition.

ISBN: 978-0-19-906185-3

Seventh Impression 2013

Adapted by arrangement with Oxford University Press, India,
for sale in Pakistan only and not for export therefrom

Written by Shamlu Dudeja

Illustrations by Rajkumar Ghosh, Amit John, and Nitin Chawla

Cover illustration by Amit John

Printed in Malaysia
Published by
Ameena Saiyid, Oxford University Press
No. 38, Sector 15, Korangi Industrial Area,
PO Box 8214, Karachi-74900, Pakistan

Preface

When children enter school, most of them have a certain amount of fascination for numbers and shapes. Quite often, however, this fascination is short-lived as they face a barrage of confusing facts and concepts in the classroom. This leads to rote learning which is devoid of any real joy and as a consequence most students drift away from the subject. The root cause for this unfortunate situation is lack of practical work, both inside and outside the classroom, and teaching from textbooks that do not excite a child's mind.

This successful series has always aimed to increase this fascination for numbers in the young minds by introducing mathematical skills to them in a manner in which they are encouraged to use as many senses as possible including hearing, seeing and doing. As a result, they get a sense of discovery and excitement as they move from one level of knowledge to the higher one and in the process enhance their learning skills too.

This revised **New Countdown** strongly reinforces this objective by presenting the magic of numbers in a friendly, fun-filled environment (the Play-way Method) where children hear, see and touch everyday objects, ask questions and get answers, and end up working in the books. With child-centred, cheerful pictures, and additional fun-filled worksheets and maths lab activities, this series promises to create a 'learning environment' rather than a 'teaching' one for the child.

New Countdown Second Edition is a carefully structured and graded mathematics course comprising ten books from the two levels of kindergarten to class 8. The pattern followed in the entire series ensures development in all areas of a child's growth through basic multi-focal knowledge, emphasizing number skills and mathematical concepts. It conforms to the broad guidelines set by all major syllabuses.

Key features

✧ Clear presentation of key mathematical concepts
✧ Solved examples of all concepts
✧ Plenty of practice exercises
✧ Review pages at the end of each section as also the book
✧ Colourful illustrations
✧ Worksheets to test the child's grasp of concepts
✧ Maths lab activities to help build concepts through different activities

OXFORD
UNIVERSITY PRESS

Contents

OXFORD
UNIVERSITY PRESS

OXFORD
UNIVERSITY PRESS

OXFORD
UNIVERSITY PRESS

Getting Ready

▶ 1. Number pyramids.

Look carefully at this number pyramid:

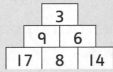

```
      3
    9   6
  17  8  14
```

Can you see how the numbers are linked?

3 + 6 = 9; 9 + 8 = 17; 8 + 6 = 14

Yes, the number in the box directly **above** a pair of numbers equals the **difference** between those two numbers.

Complete these pyramids.

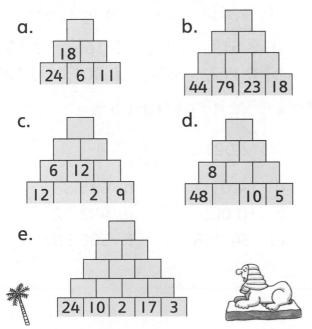

a.
```
    18
  24  6  11
```

b.
```
  44  79  23  18
```

c.
```
    6  12
  12    2   9
```

d.
```
     8
  48    10  5
```

e.
```
  24 10  2  17  3
```

Now write the number equations for each pyramid.

▶ 2. Maths in your head! Work out the answers in your head, then write them in your notebook.

a. The LCM of 6 and 9 = _____

b. If a square carpet covers an area of 25 m², each side is _____ m long.

c. A rectangle 11.5 cm long and 4.5 cm wide has a perimeter of _____ cm.

d. In △ABC, ∠BAC = 70°, and ∠ABC = 45°. What will ∠BCA be equal to?

e. What is the fraction form of (i) 0.2? (ii) 0.05? (iii) 0.008?

f. If five pens cost Rs 20.25, how much do two pens cost?

g. VI + III = _____ in Arabic numerals.

h. 8659 ÷ 100 = _____ r _____

i. A room 13 m long and 11 m broad has an area of _____ m².

j. $2\frac{1}{2} + 4\frac{2}{3}$ = _____ in decimal form.

k. The HCF of 28 and 56 = _____.

1

OXFORD
UNIVERSITY PRESS

Getting Ready

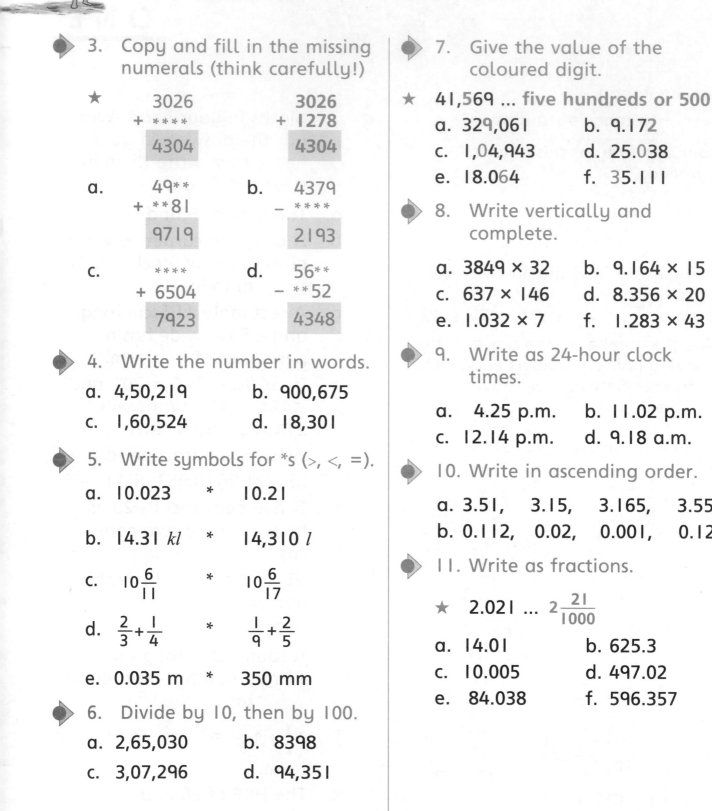

3. Copy and fill in the missing numerals (think carefully!)

★
```
    3026            3026
  + ****          + 1278
   4304            4304
```

a.
```
    49**
  + **81
   9719
```

b.
```
    4379
  - ****
    2193
```

c.
```
    ****
  + 6504
   7923
```

d.
```
    56**
  - **52
    4348
```

4. Write the number in words.
   a. 4,50,219   b. 900,675
   c. 1,60,524   d. 18,301

5. Write symbols for *s (>, <, =).
   a. 10.023   *   10.21

   b. 14.31 *kl*   *   14,310 *l*

   c. $10\frac{6}{11}$ * $10\frac{6}{17}$

   d. $\frac{2}{3}+\frac{1}{4}$ * $\frac{1}{9}+\frac{2}{5}$

   e. 0.035 m   *   350 mm

6. Divide by 10, then by 100.
   a. 2,65,030   b. 8398
   c. 3,07,296   d. 94,351

7. Give the value of the coloured digit.

★ 41,569 ... five hundreds or 500
   a. 329,061   b. 9.172
   c. 1,04,943   d. 25.038
   e. 18.064   f. 35.111

8. Write vertically and complete.

   a. 3849 × 32   b. 9.164 × 15
   c. 637 × 146   d. 8.356 × 20
   e. 1.032 × 7   f. 1.283 × 43

9. Write as 24-hour clock times.

   a. 4.25 p.m.   b. 11.02 p.m.
   c. 12.14 p.m.   d. 9.18 a.m.

10. Write in ascending order.

   a. 3.51,   3.15,   3.165,   3.55
   b. 0.112,   0.02,   0.001,   0.121

11. Write as fractions.

   ★ 2.021 ... $2\frac{21}{1000}$

   a. 14.01   b. 625.3
   c. 10.005   d. 497.02
   e. 84.038   f. 596.357

12. Write in long division form and complete.

   a. 693 ÷ 47   b. 16.848 ÷ 8
   c. 875 ÷ 56   d. 109.15 ÷ 3

13. Write in order, starting with the smallest.

   a. $\frac{1}{2}$ m, 3.5 cm, 25 mm, 20 cm

   b. $\frac{3}{4}$ m, 1.7 m, 120 cm, 35 cm

   c. $\frac{4}{5}$ l, 27 l,   430 l,   3.2 l

14. Write the HCF of:

   a. 27 and 45   b. 56 and 72
   c. 25 and 35   d. 60 and 40

15. Tick the numbers that are divisible by 9.

   a. 3,06,054   b. 30,906
   c. 1,18,275   d. 2,57,084

16. Add or subtract.

   a. $3\frac{3}{5} + 2\frac{3}{4}$ b. $10\frac{1}{8} - 4\frac{5}{6}$

   c. $5\frac{1}{5} + 6\frac{3}{10}$ d. $9\frac{2}{7} - 1\frac{13}{14}$

17. Write as decimals.

   a. $8\frac{5}{100}$ b. $7\frac{1}{2}$

   c. $6\frac{23}{1000}$ d. $9\frac{31}{250}$

   e. $4\frac{1}{10}$ f. $18\frac{3}{25}$

18. Write vertically and complete.

   a. 2,68,039 + 53,458 + 174
   b. 16 + 75,034 + 759 + 1632
   c. 1845 + 9 + 64,038 + 1,01,295

19. Using your protractor or set square, draw rectangles with sides of these lengths.

   a. 5.8 cm and 3.7 cm
   b. 9.3 cm and 5.1 cm
   c. 8.4 cm and 4.5 cm

   Draw symbols to show the right angles of your shapes. Then calculate the perimeter of each shape.

20. Draw these angles using a protractor. (Your angles can open in either direction.)

   a.   20°   b.   110°
   c. 130°   d.   90°
   e.   45°   f.   125°

21. Now draw these angles and label them.

   a. ∠PQR =   85°
   b. ∠ABC = 145°
   c. ∠RST =   90°
   d. ∠EFG =   25°
   e. ∠JKL = 120°

OXFORD
UNIVERSITY PRESS

More about Graphs: the Line Graph

We know that graphs are extremely useful in helping us to **observe differences** easily.

A column graph like this ...

Amount of pocket money

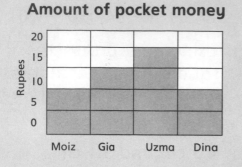

... helps us see at a glance which child gets the most pocket money.

A pie graph like this tells us immediately that pizza is the favourite food of Class 5A.

Favourite foods of Class 5A

Another very useful graph is the **line graph.** It is particularly useful when we want to measure something which is gradually **changing.**

This line graph shows the **growth of a plant** over a period of 5 days.

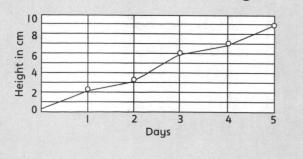

1. Look carefully at the line graph at the bottom of the previous column, and answer these questions.

   a. What was the height of the plant on the 1st day?

   b. How many cm did the plant grow between the 2nd and 5th days?

   c. How many cm did the plant grow between the 2nd and 3rd days?

   d. Between which days did the plant grow the fastest?

2. Study this line graph and answer the questions.

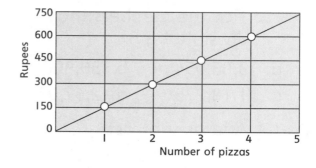

   a. What is the cost of 3 pizzas?

   b. If Sid Spacewalker has a Rs 500 note, how many pizzas can he buy?

   c. If Sid needs 25 pizzas for a party, how much money must he spend?

3. Copy and complete this line graph.

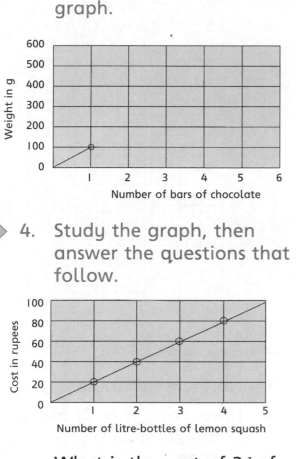

4. Study the graph, then answer the questions that follow.

a. What is the cost of 3*l* of lemon squash?

b. If you have two Rs 20 notes, can you buy 4*l* of lemon squash?

c. How much change will you get from Rs 100 when you buy 2*l* of lemon squash?

Journey of brown car from Karachi to lahore

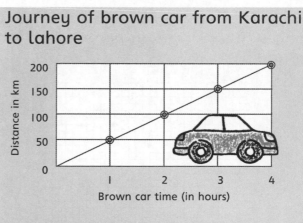

Journey of black car along Rawalpindi

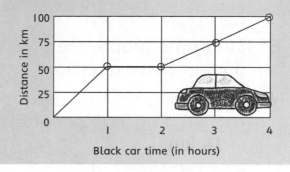

5. Use the graphs given above to answer these questions.

a. How much farther did the brown car travel than the black car?

b. Between which hours did the driver of the black car stop for lunch?

c. At the end of the 3rd hour, how far had each of the two cars travelled?

d. In which hour did the black car travel the farthest?

Line Graphs

The graph tells us about Sara Spacewalker's ride on her space-moped.

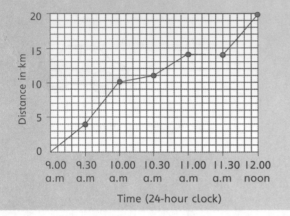

★ 6. Study the graph, then answer these questions.

★ How many km had Sara travelled by 11.00 hours?
... **14 km**

a. At what time did Sara begin her trip?

b. What was the total length of her journey in km?

c. At what time did Sara stop for a rest? How long was it before she resumed her journey?

d. How far had Sara still to go at 11.30 h?

e. At what time did Sara complete exactly half the distance of her journey?

This line graph tells us about people arriving at Qaddafi Cricket Stadium, Lahore, to watch a test match between Pakistan and England.

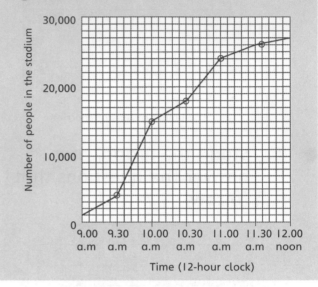

★ 7. Now answer these.

★ How many people arrived in the stadium by 9 a.m.?
... **1000**

a. When the match started at 10 a.m., how many people were in the stadium watching it?

b. How many people arrived in the stadium between 10 a.m. and 11 a.m.?

c. How many people were in the stadium when the play stopped at noon for lunch?

It is simple to plot line graphs of our own to show the **relationship** between two sets of data.

For example, Sara wants to plot a line graph to show her progress in knitting a long, woollen scarf.

First, she prepares a table setting out the two sets of data she wants to relate: (1) the length of scarf knitted and (2) the time at which the length was measured:

Length of scarf knitted in cm	3	7	12	12	18	19
Time on a 12 hr clock	8 a.m.	9 a.m.	10 a.m.	11 a.m.	12 noon	1 p.m.

Next, she prepares the framework of the graph on graph paper, thinking very carefully about how long to make the two arms, or **axes,** of the graph:

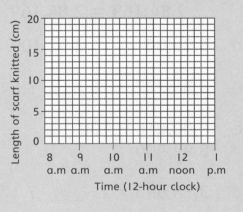

1. Draw this graph on a sheet of paper.

2. Answer these questions about the graph you have just drawn.

   a. What length of the scarf had Sara knitted by 10 a.m.?

   b. What length of the scarf was already knitted when Sara began work at 8 a.m.?

   c. By how many cm did the length of the scarf increase before Sara stopped for lunch at 1 p.m.?

   d. During which hour did Sara knit the most?

3. Aleem sells ice cream between 10 a.m. and 3 p.m. The table below shows how many ice creams he has sold at the end of each hour:

Ice creams sold	0	20	60	160	240	280
Time	10 a.m.	11 a.m.	12 noon	1 p.m.	2 p.m.	3 p.m.

Think and plot a graph to show his sales. As Sara does in her graph, make the bottom, horizontal arm of your graph showing the time, and the vertical arm showing the number of ice creams sold.

Remembering 5-Digit and 6-Digit Numbers

1. Write the value of the coloured digit.

   ★ 42,851... **2 thousands or 2000**

   a. 23,116   b. 1,20,493

   c. 94,017   d. 2,84,327

2. Write in expanded form.

   ★ 2,56,139 ...

   2,00,000 + 50,000 + 6000 + 100 + 30 + 9

   a. 40,024   c. 4,29,502

   b. 11,204   d. 6,01,751

3. Write the number, placing your commas correctly.

   ★ Two lakh, sixteen thousand, four hundred and two ...

   2,16,402

   a. Seven lakh, five hundred and thirty-eight

   b. Eight hundred and two thousand, and seventy-five

   c. One hundred and eleven thousand, and one

   d. Five lakh, five hundred and fifty-five

4. Put these numbers into International periods.

   ★ 1,60,029 ... **160,029**

   a. 5,93,162   c. 6,05,016

   b. 8,17,724   d. 2,12,212

5. Change these numbers from International to Pakistani periods.

   ★ 398,402 ... **3,98,402**

   a. 100,253   b. 999,094

   c. 412,084   d. 358,112

6. Write the successor of each number.

   ★ 682,999 ... **683,000**

   a. 1,00,029   c. 3,99,999

   b. 2,45,499   d. 3,49,999

7. Write the correct symbol (>, <, =). in each blank.

   ★ 2,84,169 _____ 2,84,169

   ... 2,84,169 = 2,84,169

   a. 3,25,001 _____ 3,52,100

   b. 3,84,292 − 10 _____ 3,84,283

   c. 9,00,010 − 100 _____ 8,99,900

   d. 3,58,666 × 2 _____ 7,17,342

What happens when we add **I more** to 999999 (the largest 6-digit number)?

On a **Pakistani place-value chart**, this is what happens:

Lakhs		Thousands		Units		
TL	L	T Th	Th	H	T	O
	9	9	9	9	9	9
						1
I	0	0	0	0	0	0

We need to use one more column, or place, to the left: the ten lakhs (TL) column.

9,99,999 + I = 10,00,000 or ten lakh

I. Write the number names.

★ **40,00,000 ... forty lakh**

a. 15,00,000

b. 60,00,000

c. 48,00,000

My name is forty lakh.

2. Write the number, placing your commas correctly.

★ Twenty-three lakh ... 23,00,000

a. Nineteen lakh

b. Eighty-four lakh

c. Seventy lakh

Ten lakh is the **smallest 7-digit number** in the Pakistani place-value system.

Here is another 7-digit number:

38,04,637

Its number name (notation) is thirty-eight lakh, four thousand, six hundred and thirty-seven.

3. Place these 7-digit numbers in Pakistani periods and write their names.

★ 19,60,283 ... nineteen lakh, sixty thousand, two hundred and eighty-three

a. 31,19,624   b. 47,03,955

c. 60,30,158   d. 80,00,206

4. Write the numbers, placing your commas carefully.

★ Sixty-four lakh, two thousand and sixty ... 64,02,060

a. Seventy-one lakh, twelve thousand, and forty-two

b. Thirty-three lakh, ninety thousand five hundred, and sixty-seven

c. Eighteen lakh, four thousand two hundred, and seventy-two

OXFORD
UNIVERSITY PRESS

We know that 1000000 is the smallest 7-digit number.

In Pakistan (and other parts of South Asia), this number is called **ten lakh** and is written as 10,00,000.

But elsewhere in the world, it has a different name, one million, and is written like this: 1,000,000.

10,00,000 = 1,000,000
(both are 7-digit numbers)

Here is the number 4385962 written in the two different ways:

1. **Pakistani** place-value chart:

Lakhs		Thousands		Units		
TL	L	T Th	Th	H	T	O
4	3	8	5	9	6	2

2. **International** place value-chart:

Millions		Thousands			Units		
TM	M	H Th	T Th	Th	H	T	O
	4	3	8	5	9	6	2

'M' means 'millions' and 'TM' means 'ten millions' (an 8-digit number!)

1. Place these in periods, first in the Pakistani way, second in the International way.

   ★ 8324967 ... 83,24,967 = 8,324,967

   a. 2905384   b. 6470317

   c. 1320059   d. 4305016

2. Write the number names.

   ★ 2,000,000 ... two million

   a. 4,000,000   b. 6,500,000

   c. 9,000,000   d. 5,620,000

   e. 8,000,000   f. 2,840,000

3. Write the number, placing your commas correctly.

   ★ Five million ... 5,000,000

   a. Two million, five hundred thousand

   b. Five million, seven hundred and forty thousand

   c. Eight million, six hundred thousand

   d. Nine million, nine hundred thousand

4. Change these numbers into International periods.

   ★ 14,67,015 ... 1,467,015

   a. 60,29,347   b. 19,03,001

   c. 25,00,123   d. 8,49,016

   e. 84,17,869   f. 14,03,970

7-Digit Numbers: Place Value

1. Look carefully at the numbers, then write the value of the coloured digit.

   ★ 49,648,123 ... six hundred thousand or 600,000

   a. 14,79,623
   b. 1,090,900
   c. 3,495,631
   d. 8,049,315
   e. 28,04,925
   f. 9,116,661

2. Read aloud, then write in words.

   ★ 75,00,065 ... seventy-five lakh and sixty-five

   a. 702,019
   b. 60,03,007
   c. 6,750,142
   d. 96,52,095

3. Write the number.

   ★ One million, two hundred and forty-seven thousand, three hundred and sixty-two

     ... 1,247,362

   a. Twenty-eight lakh, sixty thousand, seven hundred and thirteen
   b. Five million, eight thousand and twenty-three
   c. Thirty-five lakh, forty-one thousand and eighteen

4. Write in expanded form.

   ★ 6,482,113 ...
     6,000,000 + 400,000
     + 80,000 + 2000
     + 100 + 10 + 3

   a. 4,532,481
   b. 6,093,048
   c. 28,16,019
   d. 37,05,131
   e. 17,53,224
   f. 3,629,503

5. Arrange in ascending order.

   ★ 9,248,517; 9,240,715; 9,208,751

   ... 9,208,751; 9,240,715; 9,248,517

   a. 18,06,295; 18,60,995; 18,06,259
   b. 4,053,612; 4,035,812; 4,530,216; 4,033,965
   c. 24,15,396; 24,51,996; 24,05,031

6. Write the predecessor.

   ★ 32,00,000 ... 31,99,999

   a. 18,20,200
   b. 6,243,000
   c. 53,60,000
   d. 49,50,000
   e. 4,632,450
   f. 12,02,100

OXFORD
UNIVERSITY PRESS

7-Digit Numbers: Place Value

7. Write the number that matches each of these expanded forms.

★ 2,000,000 + 88,000 + 400 + 2

      = 2,088,402

a. 44,00,000 + 6000 + 300 + 10

b. 67,00,000 + 10,000 + 2000

   + 500 + 4

c. 3,000,000 + 700,000 + 40,000

   + 2000 + 60 + 9

d. 8,000,000 + 500,000 + 3000

   + 700 + 40

e. 90,00,000 + 40,000 + 6000

   + 100 + 90 + 1

f. 1,000,000 + 80,000 + 5000

   + 800 + 50 + 8

8. Read aloud, then write in words.

a. 8,096,432   b. 1,100,001

c. 64,03,115   d. 5,700,300

e. 10,01,100   f. 9,123,312

9. Arrange in descending order.

★ 1,293,401; 1,923,401; 1,239,104

1,923,401; 1,293,401; 1,239,104

a. 15,00,629; 15,00,962; 15,00,266

b. 23,14,038; 23,41,380; 23,14,381

c. 5,690,410; 5,691,410; 5,691,441

10. Write the correct symbol in each blank (>, <, =).

★ 1,250,131 _____ 12,50,311

1,250,131 < 12,50,311

a. 4,084,620 _____ 4,084,260

b. 18,50,119 _____ 18,51,119

c. 23,62,731 _____ 23,26,731

d. 5,116,290 _____ 51,16,290

e. 64,03,495 _____ 64,04,495

f. 73,02,220 _____ 7,302,220

Thinking Even B-i-g-g-e-r: 8-Digit Numbers

What happens when we add 1 more to 9999999 (the biggest 7-digit number)?

On our **Pakistani place-value chart**, something very special happens— we run out of lakhs, and need to add a new house, or period: the **House of Crores**:

Crores		Lakhs		Thousands		Units		
TC	C	TL	L	T Th	Th	H	T	O
		9	9	9	9	9	9	9
+								1
	1,	0 0,		0	0,	0	0	0

'C' means 'crores' and 'TC' (the next column to the left) means 'ten crores'—a giant-sized number with 9 digits!

1. Write the number names.

   ★ 8,00,00,000 ... **8 crore**
   a. 4,00,00,000
   b. 6,00,00,000
   c. 2,00,00,000
   d. 10,00,00,000
   e. 5,00,00,000
   f. 9,00,00,000

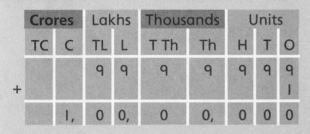

2. Write the numbers.

   ★ Three crore ... **3,00,00,000**
   a. Eight crore   b. One crore
   c. Eleven crore d. Four crore
   e. Five crore   f. Twenty crore

One crore is the **smallest 8-digit number** in the Pakistani place-value system.

When we listen to the news on the radio, or watch TV programmes about Pakistan's economy, or read newspaper articles, we often come across this word.

If **one crore** people come to hear the Prime Minister's speech, he or she will be very happy indeed!

3. The following list gives the total number of votes won by seven constituencies in Pakistan. Place each number in Pakistani periods. Which constituency received most votes?

   ★ Constituency A: 24701632
      ... **2,47,01,632**

   Constituency B: 38019478
   Constituency C: 39326301
   Constituency D: 1275317

13

OXFORD
UNIVERSITY PRESS

More about Crores

Here is another 8-digit number placed in Pakistani periods:

5,12,64,821

Its number name is "five crore, twelve lakh, sixty-four thousand, eight hundred and twenty-one"

1. Place these numbers in Pakistani periods and write their names.

   ★ 4,06,85,012 ... **Four crore, six lakh, eighty-five thousand and twelve**

   a. 67300159   b. 32456900
   c. 30846002   d. 17018037

2. Write the numbers, placing your commas carefully.

   ★ Five crore, one lakh, and sixteen ... 5,01,00,016

   a. Three crore, eleven lakh, forty-two thousand, three hundred
   b. Eight crore, thirty lakh, nineteen thousand, four hundred and sixty-one
   c. Four crore, eighty-six lakh, fifty thousand and ninety-two
   d. Six crore, forty-nine thousand, seven hundred and three
   e. Seven crore and three hundred

3. Write the value of the coloured digit.

   ★ 4,10,62,938 ... ten lakh or 10,00,000

   a. 8,15,67,032
   b. 5,00,92,475
   c. 4,73,85,693
   d. 9,87,32,777

4. Write in expanded form.

   ★ 5,26,49,032 ... 5,00,00,000 + 20,00,000 + 6,00,000 + 40,000 + 9,000 + 30 + 2

   a. 6,18,30,596   b. 5,94,03,075
   c. 7,05,12,847   d. 3,42,01,690
   e. 1,10,95,738   f. 4,00,67,143

5. Write the successor.

   ★ 1,22,16,999 ... 1,22,17,000

   a. 3,18,72,499
   b. 4,08,23,999
   c. 8,72,39,999
   d. 9,57,99,999
   e. 5,99,99,999

OXFORD
UNIVERSITY PRESS

One Crore Equals Ten Million

If we use the word 'crore' in the West, nobody will understand the meaning!

On the **International place-value chart,** the smallest 8-digit number is called **ten million:**

Millions		Thousands			Units		
TM	M	H Th	T Th	Th	H	T	O
1	0,	0	0	0,	0	0	0

Remember: one crore equals ten million.

1. Write the number names.

   ★ 46,030,100 ... **forty-six million, thirty thousand, one hundred**

   a. 38,100,580   b. 60,174,005
   c. 51,069,120   d. 25,430,756
   e. 19,405,328   f. 10,165,032

2. Place these in periods, first in the Pakistani way, second in the International way.

   ★ 40396425 ...
   (i) 4,03,96,425
   (ii) 40,396,425

   a. 38106259   b. 60054291
   c. 41965478   d. 56030201
   e. 12450031   f. 93768325

3. Write the number, placing your commas correctly.

   ★ eighteen million, four thousand and twenty-seven ... 18,004,027

   a. Thirty-one million, five hundred and ten thousand, six hundred and three
   b. Seventy-eight million, four hundred thousand, eight hundred and twelve
   c. Eighty-eight million and fifteen
   d. Twelve million, nine hundred and sixty-four thousand, two hundred and one
   e. Fifty million, three hundred and ninety thousand, seven hundred and eighty-seven

OXFORD
UNIVERSITY PRESS

8-Digit Numbers: Place Value

1. Change these numbers into International periods.

   ★ 4,02,59,603 ... **40,259,603**

   a. 6,18,92,079   b. 8,00,69,464

   c. 3,54,06,295   d. 4,27,01,695

2. Read aloud, then write in words.

   ★ 1,90,42,110 ... **one crore, ninety lakh, forty-two thousand, one hundred and ten**

   a. 85,623,005   b. 8,15,16,075

   c. 7,48,01,623   d. 30,585,624

3. Write the number.

   ★ Seventeen million, six hundred thousand and eighty-nine ... **17,600,089**

   a. Four crore, ten lakh, fifteen thousand, eight hundred and four

   b. Eighty-six million, twenty-seven thousand, three hundred and twenty

   c. One crore, ninety-four lakh, six thousand, four hundred and thirteen

4. Write the predecessor.

   ★ 35,000,000 ... **34,999,999**

   a. 18,350,000

   b. 1,38,12,100

   c. 3,04,00,000

   d. 16,800,000

5. Write in expanded form.

   ★ 47,625,105 ... **40,000,000 + 7,000,000 + 600,000 + 20,000 + 5000 + 100 + 5**

   a. 52,018,623   b. 1,29,42,060

   c. 4,53,08,492   d. 11,958,121

6. Think and write!

   a. If one crore equals _____ million, ten crore equals _____ million.

   b. One crore rupees divided equally between two charity homes equals _____ lakh rupees each.

8-Digit Numbers: Place Value

7. Arrange in ascending order.

a. 49,603,298; 49,630,928; 49,613,829

b. 3,41,06,235; 3,41,60,532; 3,41,59,332

c. 85,014,623;   85,004,632; 84,041,362;   85,011,184

8. Write the successor.

★ 43,599,999 ... **43,600,000**

a. 8,07,49,999

b. 3,01,999,999

c. 24,100,009

d. 2,48,39,999

9. Skip-counting in hundreds, write numbers in the blanks.

a. 19,643,298; ____; ____; ____; ____

b. 65,030,916; ____; ____; ____; ____

c. 37,199,834; ____; ____; ____; ____

d. 2,08,52,615; ____; ____; ____; ____

10. Write the correct symbol in each blank (<, >, =).

a. 1,29,30,142 _____ 12,930,421

b. 48,163,538 _____ 4,82,63,528

c. 7,00,15,033 _____ 70,015,033

d. 6,12,21,438 _____ 61,221,348

e. 8,64,30,295 _____ 86,430,295

f. 27,140,628 _____ 2,71,41,628

11. Write numbers in the blanks to complete each series (be very careful!).

★ 19,999,997; 19,999,998; ____; ____ ... 19,999,999; 20,000,000

a. 1,103,000; 1,104,000; ____; ____

b. 57,999,800; 57,999,900; ____; ____

c. 20,600,107; 20,700,107; ____; ____

d. 6,18,09,799; 6,18,09,899; ____; ____

e. 46,100,895; 46,100,995 ____; ____

f. 37,560,899; 37,560,999; ____; ____

Using Big Numbers: Lakhs, Crores or Millions

1. Given below are some sentences you might read in Pakistani newspapers or magazines. Change them so that visitors from abroad can understand the numbers.

★ Two crore people voted in the elections, yesterday.

... Twenty million people voted in the elections, yesterday.

a. About 4 crore children in Pakistan aged between 5 and 9 go to school.

b. Nearly five lakh people attended a giant political rally in Lahore yesterday.

c. About thirteen lakh students are enrolled in colleges and universities in Pakistan.

d. According to a census, the population of Karachi is now more than one crore.

e. Punjab is the largest province, with more than 8 crore 25 lakh people.

f. In 1990, Pakistan produced 1 crore 67 lakh tonnes of wheat.

2. Now rewrite this passage so that readers who know only the Pakistani place-value system can understand it.

All About Superglobe

Planet City, 14 March 2000 A.D. 87,268,000 people live on the beautiful purple planet of Superglobe. Of these, 45 million are women (or girls) and 42 million are men (or boys). Along with the people, live 15 million two hundred thousand super-cows and 21 million four hundred thousand super-sheep.

About 132 million tonnes of vegetables are produced each year.

Superglobe is famous for its beautiful buildings: more than 150,000 schools; 275,000 sports centres; one-and-a-half million ice cream factories and seventeen million restaurants.

Using Big Numbers : Addition

Adding very big numbers (with 7 or 8 digits) is simple, provided we are careful to write columns neatly and carefully, and to work from the ones column first:

```
  I  II  I
  2,456,138
+ 4,605,952
  7,062,090
```

When we finish adding, we must also remember to put in periods correctly.

1. Copy and complete.

a.
```
  1,984,623
+ 2,015,346
```

b.
```
  23,569,231
+  5,694,325
```

c.
```
  14,07,156
+ 25,92,843
```

d.
```
  4,468,571
+ 2,865,149
```

e.
```
  3,407,862
+ 1,374,109
```

f.
```
  15,650,192
+ 73,029,999
```

g.
```
  24,67,333
+ 18,05,438
```

h.
```
  3,48,36,117
+ 1,05,62,431
```

2. Write in vertical form and complete (be careful with columns!).

a. 3,564,121 + 2,473,565

b. 2,655,132 + 2984 + 34,103

c. 1,030,499 + 38,324 + 5687

d. 39,862 + 410,364 + 2,003,145

e. 465 + 2,49,00,321 + 1092

f. 5,62,43,018 + 32 + 51,673

g. 84,65,321 + 7495 + 1,18,626

3. Write the number which is:

★ 4000 more than 3,487,103
... 3,491,103

a. 5000 more than 20,045,624

b. 800 more than 1,26,95,382

c. 20,000 more than 14,62,834

d. 12,000 more than 2,695,148

e. 900 more than 5,624,540

Using Big Numbers: Subtraction

When doing subtraction sums with very big numbers, we are always careful with our columns:

$$2\,6,\overset{5}{4}\,\overset{1}{9}\,7,\,\overset{1}{2}\,6\,\overset{15}{4}$$
$$-\,1\,3,\,9\,4\,2,\,0\,9\,6$$
$$\overline{1\,2,\,5\,5\,5,\,1\,6\,8}$$

1. Copy and complete.

a.
```
  1,496,953
-   205,343
```

b.
```
  45,647,329
- 14,538,142
```

c.
```
  4,875,648
- 1,232,537
```

d.
```
  1,64,00,825
-    79,36,172
```

e.
```
  28,64,932
- 14,18,725
```

f.
```
  50,100,032
- 28,052,164
```

g.
```
  51,95,438
- 38,41,654
```

h.
```
  2,70,03,029
- 1,08,16,420
```

2. Now write sums to answer these.

a. From the greatest 7-digit number (Pakistani system), subtract the smallest 6-digit number.

b. Find the difference between the greatest 8-digit number (International system) and the greatest 5-digit number.

c. From the smallest 8-digit number (Pakistani system), subtract the greatest 6-digit number.

3. Write in vertical form and complete.

a. 85,231,569   –   16,829,293

b. 2,00,00,360   –   38,745

c. 4,000,351   –   25,689

d. 8,60,03,814   –   65,17,298

e. 10,000,000   –   45,692

f. 32,034,629   –   1,465,117

4. Write the number which is:

a. 2000 less than 49,840,328

b. 700 less than 7,593,400

c. 5000 less than 52,13,864

Addition and Subtraction: Word Problems

In everyday life, quite often we need to work out problems involving very big numbers—for example, huge sums of money, very large groups of people or distances between planets.

A census is a special survey in which a government employee visits every household in the country to find out **exactly** how many people there are, what type of work people are doing, whether children are attending school, and other types of useful information. In Pakistan, a fresh census is usually done every 10 years.

▷ 1. Study the table carefully.

Population of Pakistani Provinces/Areas according to the 1998 Census	
Khyber Pakhtunkhwa	17,744,321
FATA (Federally Administered Tribal Areas)	3,176,547
Punjab	73,621,441
Sindh	30,441,000
Balochistan	6,566,376
Islamabad (Federal Capital Area)	805,176

Now answer these, thinking carefully whether you should add or subtract.

a. How many more people live in Sindh than in Khyber Pakhtunkhwa?

b. After Punjab, which province has the most number of people? How many people altogether, live in this province and in the Punjab?

c. What is the total population of FATA and Sindh?

d. Which province has the least number of people? What is the difference in population between this province and the Punjab?

e. If the population of Balochistan is added to that of Islamabad, how many people are there altogether?

OXFORD
UNIVERSITY PRESS

Rounding Off

When the Pakistani Government carries out a census, it tries to count, very accurately, every person living in the country.

But often, in everyday life, we do not need to be so exact.

For example ...

If someone asks Sid his age, Sid does not answer 31 years, 4 months, 12 days, 15 hours, 3 minutes and 23 seconds! He simply says:

I am 31!

Sid has **rounded off** his age to the nearest year.

And, if you ask Sid how many people live on Superglobe, he certainly won't remember that the number is 87,688,000. But he might be able to say:

Superglobe? About 88,000,000.

Sid has **rounded off** the number to the nearest million.

Rounding off is a useful short cut. It helps us give **approximate** answers when exact answers are not needed.

For example, Kamran may have 63 marbles in his collection:

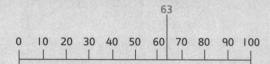

To round off a number to the nearest 10, look at the numbers in the ones place. We round down if that number is smaller than 5 and round up if it is 5 or bigger than 5. 63 is nearer to 60 than to 70. So Kamran says he has 60 marbles. He has rounded off to the nearest 10.

1. Round off these numbers to the nearest 10.

   ★ 138 ... 140
   a. 51   b. 112   c. 999
   d. 49   e. 147   f. 1253

2. Round off these numbers to the nearest 100.

   ★ 563 ...   (nearer to 600 than 500) 600
   a. 179   b. 2430   c. 9679
   d. 241   e. 6274   f. 4031

Rounding Off

Sprog Spacewalker has 145 stamps. He wants to **round off** this total to the nearest 10:

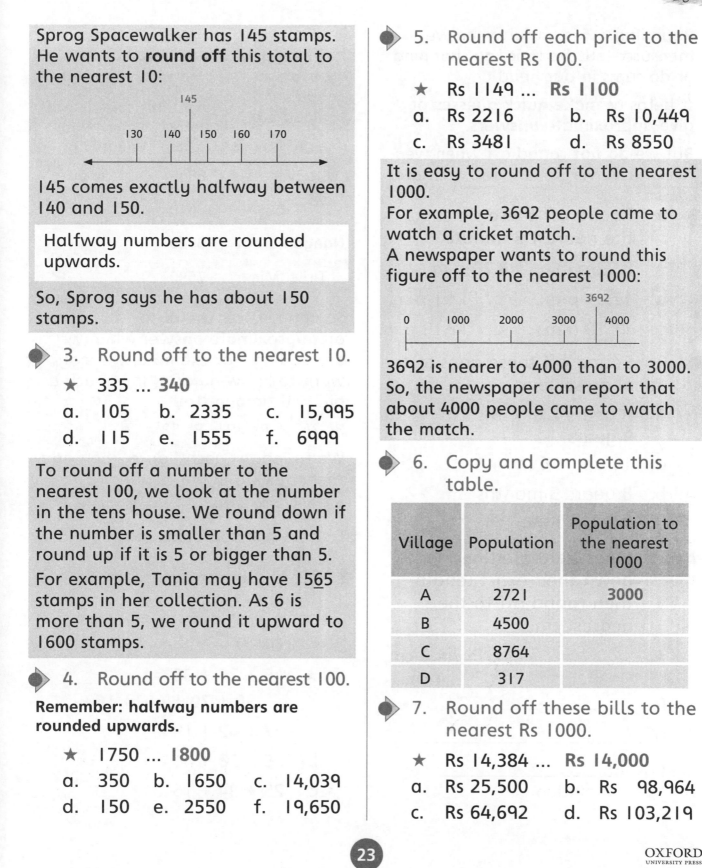

145 comes exactly halfway between 140 and 150.

Halfway numbers are rounded upwards.

So, Sprog says he has about 150 stamps.

3. Round off to the nearest 10.

★ 335 ... **340**

a. 105   b. 2335   c. 15,995

d. 115   e. 1555   f. 6999

To round off a number to the nearest 100, we look at the number in the tens house. We round down if the number is smaller than 5 and round up if it is 5 or bigger than 5.
For example, Tania may have 15<u>6</u>5 stamps in her collection. As 6 is more than 5, we round it upward to 1600 stamps.

4. Round off to the nearest 100.

Remember: halfway numbers are rounded upwards.

★ 1750 ... **1800**

a. 350   b. 1650   c. 14,039

d. 150   e. 2550   f. 19,650

5. Round off each price to the nearest Rs 100.

★ Rs 1149 ... **Rs 1100**

a. Rs 2216   b. Rs 10,449

c. Rs 3481   d. Rs 8550

It is easy to round off to the nearest 1000.
For example, 3692 people came to watch a cricket match.
A newspaper wants to round this figure off to the nearest 1000:

3692 is nearer to 4000 than to 3000. So, the newspaper can report that about 4000 people came to watch the match.

6. Copy and complete this table.

Village	Population	Population to the nearest 1000
A	2721	**3000**
B	4500	
C	8764	
D	317	

7. Round off these bills to the nearest Rs 1000.

★ Rs 14,384 ... **Rs 14,000**

a. Rs 25,500   b. Rs 98,964

c. Rs 64,692   d. Rs 103,219

23

OXFORD
UNIVERSITY PRESS

More about Rounding Off

Rounding off is useful when we measure, tell the time, go shopping or do sums in our head.

It helps us make **quick guesses** or give **approximate answers**.

But we **do not** round off when we need to be very exact and accurate.

8. Round off these times to the nearest 5 minute.

★ 8.22 a.m. ... **8.20 a.m.**

a. 12.14 p.m.   b. 1.01 p.m.

c. 11.18 a.m.   d. 12.19 p.m.

9. Round off these ages to the nearest year.

★ 9 years 2 months ... **9 years**

a. 10 years 6 months

b. 8 years 5 months

c. 7 years 6 months 2 days

10. Measure these lines, write down their exact length, then round off to the nearest cm.

★ _____ 4.2 cm, 4 cm

a. _____

b. _____

c. _____

11. Copy and complete the table.

Mountain	Height in metres	Height rounded off to nearest 100 m
Mt Everest	8848	8800
K2	8610	
Nanga Parbat	8126	
Tirich Mir	7690	

Sometimes it is useful to work out an **approximate answer** when we are adding. For example, we may want to know quickly how much a bill will amount to:

Rs 247 + Rs 29 + Rs 53 = ?

We round off each figure, then add them quickly in our head:

Rs 250 + Rs 30 + Rs 50 = Rs 330

Our total is **approximately** Rs 330.

12. Work out approximate answers to these sums by rounding off to the nearest 10.

★ 45 + 71 + 38 = _____
... 50 + 70 + 40 = 160

a. 27 + 42 + 19

b. 56 + 38 + 41

c. 25 + 34 + 16

We can round off big numbers to the nearest 10 or multiple of 10: to the nearest 100; 1000; 10,000; 100,000; or even 1,000,000 (depending on the size of our number.)

Let us take the population figure for Khyber Pakhtunkhwa 17,744,321, and round it off:

1. to the nearest 10	17,744,320
2. to the nearest 100	17,744,300
3. to the nearest 1000	17,744,000
4. to the nearest 10000	17,740,000
5. to the nearest 100,000	17,700,000
6. to the nearest 1,000,000	18,000,000

13. Round these off to the nearest 10,000.

★ 386,114 ... **390,000**

a. 265,000

b. 1,432,161

c. 148,732

d. 2,123,945

e. 384,239

f. 5,648,021

g. 752,169

h. 6,011,933

14. Round these off to the nearest 100,000:

★ 1,462,315 ... 1,500,000

a. 2,637,002

b. 1,918,727

15. Copy and complete this table.

Item	Cost in Rs	Cost to the nearest Rs million
Hospital	6,500,000	7,000,000
Stadium	7,362,000	
Hotel	5,964,310	
School	1,093,999	

16. Refer to page 21 and answer these questions.

★ What is the population of Sindh rounded off to the nearest 10,000? ... 30,440,000

a. What is Balochistan's population rounded off to the nearest 1000?

b. What is Punjab's population rounded off to the nearest million?

c. What is the population of FATA rounded off to the nearest 100,000?

d. What is Islamabad FCA's population rounded off to the nearest 100?

OXFORD
UNIVERSITY PRESS

More Work with Bigger Numbers: Multiplication

When we carry out multiplications involving big numbers, we must be careful and accurate at every step:

```
        5983
    ×    475
  _____
       29915    (5983 × 5)
      418,810   (5983 × 70)
    2,393,200   (5983 × 400)
  _____
    2,841,925
```

1. Copy and complete.

a.
```
      1231
   ×   540
```

b.
```
      6099
   ×   487
```

c.
```
      3614
   ×   353
```

d.
```
      7536
   ×   396
```

e.
```
      6148
   ×   469
```

f.
```
      2984
   ×   455
```

g.
```
      2405
   ×   321
```

h.
```
      1879
   ×   628
```

2. Write vertically and complete.

a. 3847 × 431   b. 7346 × 398

c. 9625 × 855   d. 5174 × 872

e. 6098 × 627   f. 10,193 × 243

3. Solve the problems, making complete statements.

a. If a toy factory produces 2850 toy cars everyday, how many cars will be produced in a year of 296 working days?

b. If Naseem Hameed runs 6500 m every day as part of her training programme, how many metres will she run in the course of one year? How many km is that altogether?

c. A school uniform at Ameen High School costs Rs 1325. If there are 567 children at the school, what will the total bill for all the children's uniforms be?

Working with very big dividends is simple, provided we go carefully step by step:

Our example: **826,934 ÷ 56**

How many 56s in 82? 1

How many 56s in 266?
Our guess is 4:
56 × 4 = 224 ✓

How many 56s in 429?
Our guess is 7:
56 × 7 = 392 ✓

How many 56s in 373?
Our guess is 6:
56 × 6 = 336 ✓

```
              14,766 r 38
        56 ) 826,934
             56
             266
             224
             429
             392
             373
             336
             374
             336
             r = 38
```

Answer = 14,766 r 38 or 14,766 $\frac{38}{56}$

1. Copy and complete, working very carefully.

   a. 29) 32,497

   b. 19) 281,425

   c. 24) 18,726

   d. 23) 425,662

   e. 35) 51,972

   f. 45) 784,695

2. Write each in long division form and complete.

   a. 6295 ÷ 31   b. 85,177 ÷ 81

   c. 14,038 ÷ 87   d. 47,072 ÷ 67

   e. 35,764 ÷ 59   f. 8706 ÷ 95

3. Write quotients in the blanks after solving each division mentally.

   a. 5200 ÷ 10 = _____

   b. 3800 ÷ 19 = _____

   c. 6600 ÷ 66 = _____

   d. 7200 ÷ 24 = _____

   e. 10,000 ÷ 50 = _____

   f. 65,000 ÷ 100 = _____

4. Now solve these.

   a. 2,603,420 ÷ 25

   b. 3,192,633 ÷ 27

   c. 5,753,119 ÷ 43

OXFORD
UNIVERSITY PRESS

Division: 3-Digit Divisors

We follow exactly the same steps when we work with 3-digit divisors (or even bigger ones), as we did for 2-digit divisors:

Our example: **483,759 ÷ 381**

How many 381s in 483? Easy: 1!

How many 381s in 1027? Our guess: 3
381 × 3 = 1143 ×
381 × 2 = 762 ✓

How many 381s in 2655? Guess: 7
381 × 7 = 2667 ×
381 × 6 = 2286 ✓

How many 381s in 3999? Guess: 9
381 × 9 = 3429 ✓

```
              1269 r 270
        _____
  381 ) 483,759
         381
         1027
          762
         2655
         2286
         3699
         3429
        r = 270
```

Answer = 1269, r 270 or 1269 $\frac{270}{381}$

1. Copy and complete, working as carefully as you can.

   a. 248) 32,561

   b. 187) 29,364

   c. 330) 45,695

   d. 485) 50,678

2. Write in long division form and complete.

   a. 46,028 ÷ 384

   b. 52,169 ÷ 416

   c. 75,673 ÷ 649

   d. 34,396 ÷ 457

   e. 28,932 ÷ 535

   f. 15,721 ÷ 464

   g. 56,439 ÷ 719

   h. 49,868 ÷ 637

3. Work out the division in your head, then write quotients in the blanks.

   a. 360,000 ÷ 200   = _____

   b. 480,000 ÷ 400   = _____

   c. 695,000 ÷ 695   = _____

   d. 560,000 ÷ 140   = _____

   e. 738,000 ÷ 1000   = _____

   f. 210,000 ÷ 7000   = _____

   Write your answers as fractions.

Word Problems

1. Read these carefully, and decide whether you should multiply or divide in each case. Then, solve the problems, making complete statements.

    a. Jumbo Fancy Stores wants to place an order for firecrackers. If one box contains 144 firecrackers, how many boxes must the shop order for a stock of 100,080 firecrackers?

    b. The Punjab Government wants to build new homes for 382 homeless families. If each home costs Rs 4,00,960, how much will the project cost altogether?

    c. School children in Karachi raise Rs 40,575 through a sponsored marathon race. If the collection is shared between 520 needy families, how much does each family get, and how much money will be left over?

    d. Superpop soft drinks factory employs 267 people. If each worker receives Rs 2384 as wages every month, what is the total wage bill (i) for one month, (ii) for the whole year?

2. Help Sid work out these word problems, making complete statements.

    a. If Sid's rocket travels a distance of 756,600 km in 240 hours, how many km does it travel in one hour?

    b. During his trip, Sara knits a bright, orange scarf at the rate of 469 mm every hour. If her trip lasts 8 days and if Sara sleeps only 5 hours a day, how much of the scarf will she have knitted by the end of the trip?

    c. If each of the 614 Superglobe residents eats 83250 g of vegetables in a year, what is the total weight of vegetables eaten (in kg)?

OXFORD
UNIVERSITY PRESS

1. Using graph paper, plot a line graph to show the number of people who visited Lahore Zoo during the first six months of 2004.

Number of visitors	1000	2500	3000	3500	4500	5000
Month	Jan	Feb	Mar	Apr	May	June

   a. Why do you think so many people visited the Zoo in May and June?

   b. What is the difference between the number of visitors in February and May?

   c. What is the the total number of visitors in January and February?

2. Write in expanded form.

   a. 962,430

   b. 10,720,482

   c. 2,464,209

   d. 4,67,30,141

3. Write each number in Pakistani periods.

   a. 6050038   b. 85329861

4. Rewrite each number in International periods.

   a. 4624561   b. 60405645

5. Write vertically and complete.

   a. 4,695,132 + 69,549 + 5905
   b. 16,80,519 − 8,93,745
   c. 16,213 × 264

6. Write in long division form and complete.

   a. 462,391 ÷ 384
   b. 381,684 ÷ 465

7. Round off to the nearest 10.

   a. 269   b. 8490   c. 7851

8. Round off to the nearest 100.

   a. 506   b. 6952   c. 45,023

9. Round off to the nearest 1000.

   a. 11,425

   b. 438,421

   c. 6,846,680

Bills: Working with Larger Sums of Money

This is one month's bill of food for the Shooting Star Restaurant at the Galaxy Superstore:

GALAXY SUPERSTORE			
Outer Space			
Customer's Name: S. Spacewalker			
Date: 1.11.99			
Quan-tity	Item	Cost per unit	Total cost
20 Pkts	Noodles	Rs 20.00	Rs 400.00
18 kg	Sugar	Rs 60.00	Rs 1080.00
5 kg	Butter	Rs 80.00	Rs 400.00
84	Chocobar	Rs 15.00	Rs 1260.00
100 *l*	Milk	Rs 45.00	Rs 4500.00
		Grand Total	Rs 7640.00

1. Prepare bills for these customers at Galaxy Superstore.

   a. **Mandy Moon**: $6\frac{1}{2}$ kg of rice at Rs 75 per kg, $3\frac{1}{4}$ kg of grapes at Rs 40.00 per kg; 25 packets of washing powder at Rs 80 per packet; $3\frac{1}{2}$ *l* of oil at Rs 125 per *l*.

   b. **Linda Lightyear**: $8\frac{3}{4}$ kg of wheat flour at Rs 36 per kg; 8 packets of biscuits at Rs 23 per packet; $2\frac{1}{2}$ kg of carrots at Rs 25 per kg; 1.75 kg of potatoes at Rs 30 per kg.

2. Now prepare bills for customers at Super-Zoom Garage. Make your bills wider than before, because you will be working with larger sums of money.

   a. **Sara Spacewalker**: 2 space-bikes costing Rs 12,614 each; a new lamp costing Rs 859.50; 23 *l* of petrol at Rs 48.40 per *l*.

   b. **Veena Venus**: 1 Lunar moped costing Rs 14,832.50; 4 space helmets costing Rs 219.60 each; 6 spare wheels at Rs 347.50 each.

3. This bill has a mistake! Find the mistake, then rewrite and work out the correct amounts.

Customer: Sara S.		Date: 1.11.99	
Quan-tity	Item	Cost per unit	Total cost
$8\frac{1}{2}$ kg	Rice	Rs 64.00	Rs 604.00
4 *l*	Oil	Rs 86.00	Rs 244.00
$4\frac{3}{4}$ kg	Tomatoes	Rs 30.00	Rs 47.50
12 kg	Mangoes	Rs 50.00	Rs 400.00
		Grand Total	Rs 1295.50

OXFORD
UNIVERSITY PRESS

The Four Operations: Ordering (Simplification)

We now know how to **add**, **subtract**, **multiply** and divide using very big numbers. But so far we've been doing only one of these **four operations** in one problem. For example:

$$\begin{array}{r} 1\,4\,6,3\,2\,9 \\ +\ \ 8\,4,6\,5\,1 \\ \hline 2\,3\,0,9\,8\,0 \end{array}$$
or $384 \times 100 = 38,400$

Sometimes, however, we need to do **two or more of the four operations** to solve a sum.
Look at this example:

$$9 - 6 \div 3 \times 2 + 1 = ?$$

We need to carry out all four operations to solve this problem. But in what order should we proceed?
Let us see what happens when we solve this in 3 different ways:

Solution 1	
1. We subtract first	$9 - 6 = 3$
2. We divide next:	$3 \div 3 = 1$
3. We multiply:	$1 \times 2 = 2$
4. Last, we add:	$2 + 1 = 3$
	Answer = 3

Solution 2	
1. We add:	$2 + 1 = 3$
2. We multiply:	$3 \times 3 = 9$
3. We divide:	$6 \div 9 = \frac{6}{9} = \frac{2}{3}$
4. Last, we subtract:	$9 - \frac{2}{3} = 8\frac{1}{3}$
	Answer = $8\frac{1}{3}$

Solution 3	
1. We divide:	$6 \div 3 = 2$
2. We multiply:	$2 \times 2 = 4$
3. We subtract:	$9 - 4 = 5$
4. We add:	$5 + 1 = 6$
	Answer = 6

For the same problem, $9 - 6 \div 3 \times 2 + 1$, we got three different answers! From this we can see how important it is to carry out the four operations in the correct order.

In maths, it has become the rule or **convention** to do the four operations in this order:
÷ **Division first**
× **Multiplication second**
+ **Addition third**
− **Subtraction last**
DMAS for short!

This rule or convention makes it simpler for us to solve such problems; we call it the **simplification rule**. To remember DMAS, say "Do Musicians Always Sing?"

1. Using the simplification rule, DMAS, solve these.

★ $9 + 3 \times 4$ ...
(multiply before adding)
$3 \times 4 = 12$ (next add)
$9 + 12 = 21$
Answer = 21

a. $8 + 4 - 3$ b. $8 \div 2 + 12$
c. $6 \times 5 - 5$ d. $10 - 3 \div 3$
e. $11 + 2 \times 8$ f. $12 \div 4 \times 5$
g. $30 + 6 \div 3$ h. $16 + 8 \div 2$

2. Now simplify these, using the DMAS rule.

★ 16 − 8 ÷ 4 ...

(first divide) 8 ÷ 4 = 2

(next subtract) 16 − 2 = 14

Answer = 14

a. 12 × 6 ÷ 3   b. 15 × 42 ÷ 14

c. 84 ÷ 7 × 10   d. 108 ÷ 12 + 46

e. 14 + 21 ÷ 3   f. 20 − 16 ÷ 4

g. 58 − 24 ÷ 8   h. 17 + 5 × 20

We follow the same DMAS rule when we work with 3 different operations.
For example: 6 + 2 × 4 − 8

What we do	Result
1. We multiply: 2 × 4 = 8	6 + 8 − 8
2. We add: 6 + 8 = 14	14 − 8
3. We subtract: 14 − 8 = 6	6
Answer: 6 + 2 × 4 − 8 = 6	

3. Now simplify these.

a. 3 × 2 + 8 − 5

b. 128 ÷ 4 + 12 × 5

c. 6 × 5 + 12 ÷ 4

d. 18 × 6 ÷ 2 − 24

4. Remember your DMAS rule and simplify these.

a. 7 + 6 ÷ 2 × 18

b. 5 × 15 ÷ 3 + 49

c. 121 ÷ 11 + 5 × 20

d. 8 × 14 ÷ 7 − 10

e. 84 ÷ 12 × 3 − 6

Now, work this out:

12 × 4 + 6 ÷ 2 − 11

What we do	Result
1. We divide: 6 ÷ 2 = **3**	12 × 4 + 3 − 11
2. We multiply: 12 × 4 = **48**	48 + 3 − 11
3. We add: 48 + 3 = **51**	51 − 11
4. We subtract: 51 − 11 = **40**	51 − 11 = **40**
Answer: 12 × 4 + 6 ÷ 2 − 11 = 40	

5. Think carefully, then simplify.

a. 18 + 4 × 6 ÷ 2 − 9

b. 25 ÷ 5 × 8 + 6 − 12

c. 31 + 24 ÷ 8 × 9 − 39

d. 45 ÷ 5 + 7 × 11 − 20

Simplification: Using Brackets

Sid Spacewalker is arranging delicious moon-cakes on plates ready for a party. He takes 4 plates and puts 2 cakes on each. Then Sara shouts from the kitchen that Sid should put an extra cake (2 + 1) on each plate. Sid does so:

Sid has put 4 plates × (2 + 1) cakes out altogether.

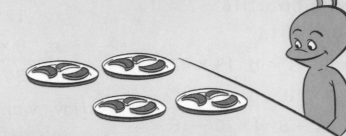

How many cakes? 4 × (2 + 1)
= 4 × 3
= **12 cakes altogether**.

But suppose Sid had written his problem like this: 4 × 2 + 1.
And suppose he had simplified his sum by using the DMAS rule.

First, he would have multiplied: 4 × 2 + 1
= 8 + 1

Then, he would have added: **8 + 1 = 9**
He would have got a completely different answer!

Once again, we see how the answers of problems involving more than one operation depend very much on the **order** in which we carry out the operations.

Sid knew he had to add **before** multiplying to see how many cakes he had put out. He knew this because he had put **brackets** around the addition part of the sum.

The brackets told him which part to work out first.

Look at these examples:

| 1. (8 − 1) × 7
= 7 × 7
= 49 | 2. 8 − 1 × 7
= 8 − 7
= 1 | | 1. (10 − 8) ÷ 2
= 2 ÷ 2
= 1 | 2. 10 − 8 ÷ 2
= 10 − 4
= 6 |

OXFORD
UNIVERSITY PRESS

Brackets help us to solve problems involving two or more operations by telling us which part of the simplification to do first, by **grouping some numbers together**.
Therefore, brackets are also called **grouping symbols**.
The most common bracket used in maths is the **round bracket**.

6. Copy and complete these. Work out the operations inside the brackets first.

   ★ $4 + (8 \times 3) \ldots 4 + (24)$
   $$= 28$$

   a. $(3 \times 7) + 12$ b. $(9 + 22) \times 4$

   c. $8 \times (12 + 16)$ d. $14 + (18 \times 3)$

7. Now copy and complete these.

   ★ $(9 - 3) \times 8 \ldots (9 - 3) = 6$
   $$(6) \times 8 = 48$$

   a. $5 \times (8 - 1)$ b. $6 \times (18 \div 9)$

   c. $(6 \times 9) - 18$ d. $(9 \times 10) \div 45$

8. Now simplify these sums involving fractions, using the brackets to help you.

   ★ $\dfrac{3}{11} + \left(\dfrac{8}{11} - \dfrac{1}{11}\right) \ldots = \dfrac{3}{11} + \left(\dfrac{7}{11}\right)$
   $$= \dfrac{10}{11}$$

   a. $\left(\dfrac{7}{8} + \dfrac{3}{8}\right) - \dfrac{5}{8}$ b. $\left(\dfrac{5}{7} - \dfrac{2}{7}\right) + \dfrac{2}{7}$

   c. $\dfrac{4}{9} - \left(\dfrac{7}{9} - \dfrac{2}{9}\right)$ d. $\dfrac{8}{15} + \left(\dfrac{12}{15} - \dfrac{7}{15}\right)$

9. Work the same way with decimal fractions.

   ★ $(0.5 + 0.2) \times 4 \ldots (0.7) \times 4$
   $$= 2.8$$

   a. $(5.0 - 0.5) \times 2$

   b. $8 \times (4.0 - 3.5)$

   c. $(9.6 - 7.2) \times 4$

   d. $16 \div (8.3 - 4.3)$

10. Think carefully. Put brackets in the correct places to make these statements true.

    a. $2 \times 2 \times 2 - 2 = 0$

    b. $2 + 2 + 2 \div 2 = 5$

    c. $18 - 6 \div 3 = 4$

OXFORD
UNIVERSITY PRESS

Simplification: Brackets

So far, we've used brackets in a string of numbers involving only two operations: for example, addition and subtraction.

Brackets are also very helpful when there are three or even four operations to be handled.

To help us decide the order of operations, we use three different types of brackets:

1. The **round bracket**: $(\;)$

2. The **curly bracket**: $\{ \; \}$
   and

3. The **square bracket**: $[\;]$

If we find all three types of brackets used at the same time, we simplify in this order:

1. **Round brackets first**,
2. **Curly next**, and
3. **Square brackets last**

For example,

$60 - [48 - \{16 + (8 - 4)\}]$

$= 60 - [48 - \{16 + (4)\}]$

$= 60 - [48 - \{16 + 4\}]$

$= 60 - [48 - \{20\}]$

$= 60 - [48 - 20]$

$= 60 - 28$

$= 32$ (Answer)

11. Working carefully, copy and simplify.

★ $4 + [15 - \{7 + (6 \div 2)\}]$
$= 4 + [15 - \{7 + (3)\}]$
$= 4 + [15 - \{7 + 3\}]$
$= 4 + [15 - \{10\}]$
$= 4 + 5$
$= 9$

a. $24 - [5 + \{8 - (9 - 6)\}]$
b. $2 \times [18 - \{6 + (9 \div 3)\}]$
c. $[100 - \{80 \div (20 \times 2)\}] + 3$
d. $80 + [10 \times \{16 - (8 \div 2)\}]$
e. $39 - [6 + \{5 - (6 - 3)\}]$
f. $10 \div [3 + \{5 - (12 \div 4)\}]$

12. Now simplify these. Remember that while adding and subtracting unlike fractions, you need to find the common denominator.

★ $\dfrac{5}{6} + \left(\dfrac{1}{2} + \dfrac{3}{4}\right) = \dfrac{5}{6} + \left(\dfrac{2}{4} + \dfrac{3}{4}\right)$

$= \dfrac{5}{6} + \dfrac{5}{4}$

$= \dfrac{10}{12} + \dfrac{15}{12} = \dfrac{25}{12}$

$= \dfrac{25}{12}$ or $2\dfrac{1}{12}$

a. $\dfrac{7}{8} + \left(\dfrac{1}{3} + \dfrac{5}{6}\right)$

b. $\left(\dfrac{3}{8} + \dfrac{3}{4}\right) + \left(\dfrac{5}{8} - \dfrac{1}{4}\right)$

c. $\dfrac{3}{5} + \left(\dfrac{7}{10} - \dfrac{1}{4}\right)$

d. $\dfrac{3}{10} + \left(\dfrac{4}{5} - \dfrac{1}{15}\right)$

Remember the sequence:
(Round) brackets first
{Curly} brackets next
[Square] brackets last

13. Simplify these and reduce your answer to its lowest terms.

★ $\frac{1}{2} + \left\{ 2\frac{1}{4} - \left(\frac{1}{3} + \frac{1}{6} \right) \right\}$

$= \frac{1}{2} + \left\{ 2\frac{1}{4} - \frac{3}{6} \right\}$

$= \frac{1}{2} + \left\{ \frac{9}{4} - \frac{3}{6} \right\}$

$= \frac{1}{2} + \left\{ \frac{27}{12} - \frac{6}{12} \right\}$

$= \frac{6}{12} + \frac{21}{12}$

$= \frac{27}{12} = 2\frac{3}{12} = 2\frac{1}{4}$

a. $10\frac{1}{10} + \left[4 - \left\{ \frac{7}{10} + \left(\frac{1}{5} + \frac{1}{4} \right) \right\} \right]$

b. $6 - \left[\frac{2}{5} + \left\{ 3\frac{1}{4} - \left(\frac{3}{8} + \frac{1}{2} \right) \right\} \right]$

c. $3\frac{1}{4} - \left\{ \frac{5}{8} + \left(2\frac{1}{2} - \frac{3}{4} \right) \right\}$

14. Now, simplify these.

a. $100 \times \{15 + (1.6 + 2.3)\}$

b. $\{18 - (4.2 - 1.4)\} \times 1000$

c. $[\{9.1 + (3 \times 20)\} \times 2] + 100$

15. Now simplify these sums involving decimal fractions. Remember to place your decimal points carefully.

★ $2.8 + \{3.61 - (1.12 + 2.34)\}$
... $1.12 + 2.34 = 3.46$
$= 2.8 + \{3.61 - (3.46)\}$
$= 2.8 + \{0.15\}$
$\quad 2.8 + 0.15 = 2.95$

a. $7.3 - \{1.4 + (0.92 + 1.63)\}$

b. $\{3 \times (1.59 + 2.01)\} + 100.22$

c. $100 \times [12 - \{6.2 + (1.3 + 2.6)\}]$

We can use brackets to simplify word problems. For example, if Sid has Rs 156 and buys a bag for Rs 65 and a pen for Rs 20, how much money is left with him?
Rs 156 − (Rs 65 + Rs 20)
= Rs 156 − 85 = Rs 71

16. Simplify these.

a. Arif shares a chocolate bar with his two brothers. He gives one brother $\frac{1}{3}$ of the bar and the other brother $\frac{1}{4}$ of the bar. How much does he keep for himself?

b. In a special offer at Sid's supermarket, music CDs which usually cost Rs 32.50 are reduced in price by Rs 5. If a customer buys six CDs, how much will they cost him?

Area

1. Write the area, in cm², of each shape shown below.

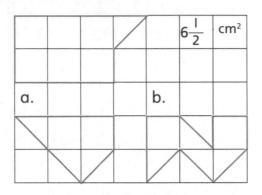

$6\frac{1}{2}$ cm²

a.

b.

2. On a paper with centimetre squares, draw these shapes.

★ A square ... with an area of 9 cm²

a. A rectangle with an area of 8 cm².

b. Any shape with an area of $10\frac{1}{2}$ cm².

c. A square with an area of 16 cm².

d. A rectangle with an area of 15 cm².

3. Copy and complete this table.

Rectangle		Area	Perimeter
length	breadth		
5 cm	2 cm	10 cm²	14 cm
16 cm	10 cm		
21 cm	3 cm		

4. Use multiplication to work out the area of these gardens.

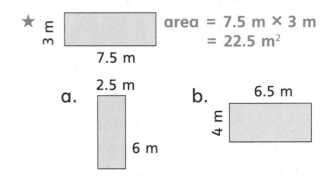

★ 3 m — 7.5 m — area = 7.5 m × 3 m = 22.5 m²

a. 2.5 m — 6 m

b. 6.5 m — 4 m

Now, work out the *perimeter* of each garden.

5. Solve these problems in your notebook.

a. If the area of a carpet is 32 m² and its breadth is 4 m, what is the length?

b. A builder has enough bricks to construct a rectangular compound wall with a perimeter of 96 m. If one side of the wall is 30 m, what is the width of the other side?

In Book 4, Sid Spacewalker showed us the floor plan of his luxurious Moon House. Each of its rooms was **rectangular** in shape, and so it was easy for us to calculate the area of every room.

But very often we need to measure the areas of shapes which are **not** simple **squares** or **rectangles**:

For example, here is the floor plan of Mick Moon's living room:

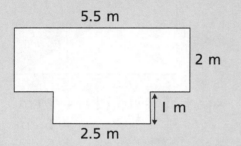

How can we calculate its area? Divide the shape into two rectangles.

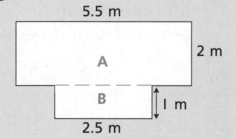

Area of A = 5.5 m × 2 m = 11.0 m²
Area of B = 2.5 m × 1 m = 2.5 m²
The total area of the room = 11.0 m²
                          + 2.5 m²
                          = 13.5 m²

The area of Mick Moon's living room is 13.5 m².

1. Work out these floor areas by dividing the shapes into rectangles.

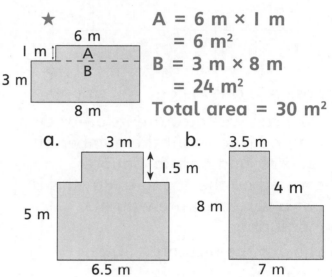

★

A = 6 m × 1 m
  = 6 m²
B = 3 m × 8 m
  = 24 m²
Total area = 30 m²

a.

b.

2. Mandy Moon, who is an architect, has designed a new school building. Work out the area of each room in it.

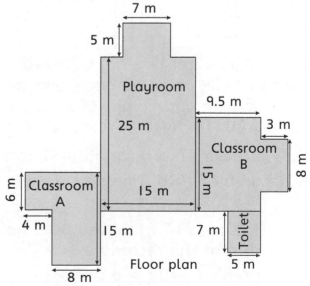

Floor plan

What is the total area covered by the school building?

OXFORD
UNIVERSITY PRESS

Area: Triangles

Look at this **right-angled triangle** ABC, on a centimetre grid:

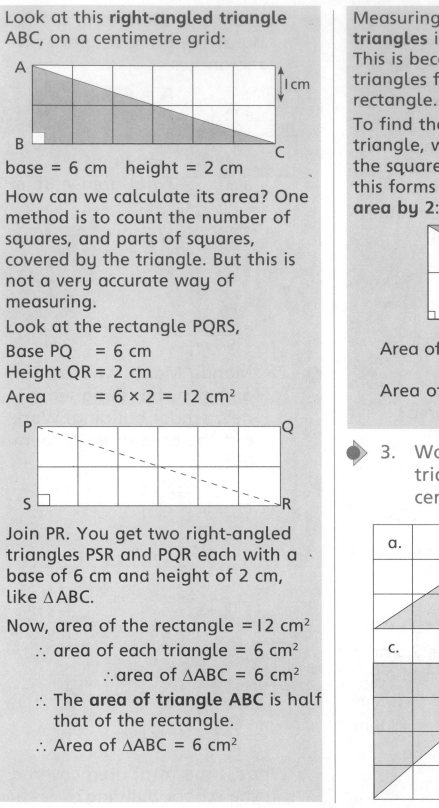

base = 6 cm   height = 2 cm

How can we calculate its area? One method is to count the number of squares, and parts of squares, covered by the triangle. But this is not a very accurate way of measuring.

Look at the rectangle PQRS,

Base PQ   = 6 cm
Height QR = 2 cm
Area   = 6 × 2 = 12 cm²

Join PR. You get two right-angled triangles PSR and PQR each with a base of 6 cm and height of 2 cm, like △ABC.

Now, area of the rectangle = 12 cm²
∴ area of each triangle = 6 cm²
∴ area of △ABC = 6 cm²
∴ The **area of triangle ABC** is half that of the rectangle.
∴ Area of △ABC = 6 cm²

Measuring the areas of **right-angled triangles** is therefore very simple. This is because all right-angled triangles form half of a square or a rectangle.

To find the area of a right-angled triangle, we work out the area of the square or rectangle of which this forms one half; then **divide this area by 2**:

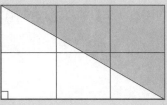

Area of rectangle = 2 cm × 3 cm
                            = 6 cm²
Area of triangle = 6 cm² ÷ 2
                            = 3 cm²

3. Work out the area of each triangle shown on a centimetre grid below.

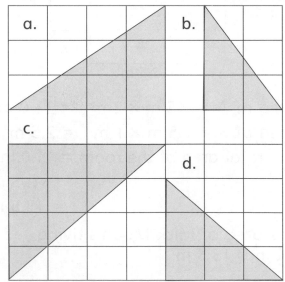

4. Work out the area of each coloured triangle.

★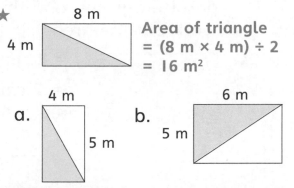

8 m

4 m

Area of triangle
= (8 m × 4 m) ÷ 2
= 16 m²

a. 4 m

5 m

b. 6 m

5 m

Now look at the shape Sid Spacewalker has drawn on squared paper:

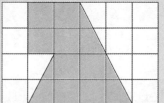

It seems impossible to measure the area of such a strange shape! But Sid has a simple solution. He divides his shape into rectangles, squares and right-angled triangles, thus:

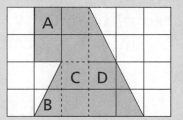

Area of square A = 2 cm × 2 cm = 4 cm²
Area of triangle B = 2 cm² ÷ 2 = 1 cm²
Area of rectangle C = 2 cm × 1 cm
　　　　　　　　　　 = 2 cm²
Area of triangle D = 8 cm² ÷ 2 = 4 cm²
Total area of the shape = 11 cm²

5. Copy these shapes carefully on to a centimetre grid. Then work out the area of each shape by dividing it into squares, rectangles and triangles.

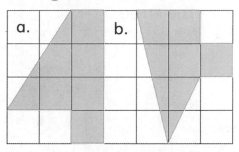

a. **b.**

Sid has now drawn a parallelogram:

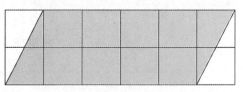

Area of parallelogram = 1 cm² +
8 cm² + 1 cm² = 10 cm²

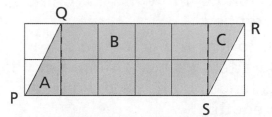

Q

B

C

R

A

P

S

But Sid also sees that if he cuts out triangle A and joins it to triangle C, he will have made a **rectangle**:

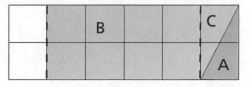

B

C

A

Area of rectangle = 8 cm² + 2 cm²
　　　　　　　　　 = 10 cm²

Area: Parallelograms

6. Copy these parallelograms carefully on a centimetre grid. Change each parallelogram into a rectangle or square of the same area and calculate the area.

★

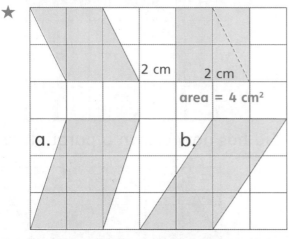

2 cm   2 cm

area = 4 cm²

a.   b.

We have seen how a parallelogram has the same area as the square or rectangle into which it can be arranged.

So to find the area of a parallelogram, we simply multiply its length by its perpendicular breadth:

length (*l*)   length (*l*)

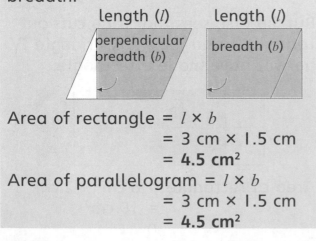

perpendicular breadth (*b*)   breadth (*b*)

Area of rectangle = *l* × *b*
             = 3 cm × 1.5 cm
             = **4.5 cm²**
Area of parallelogram = *l* × *b*
                      = 3 cm × 1.5 cm
                      = **4.5 cm²**

7. Measure the length and breadth of each of these parallelograms, and then work out the area.

★

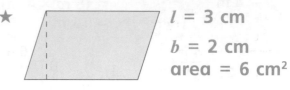

l = 3 cm

b = 2 cm

area = 6 cm²

a.   b.

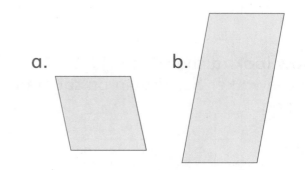

8. Measuring carefully, work out the area of each parallelogram and the area of each coloured triangle.

★ area of parallelogram
= 2 cm × 2 cm = 4 cm²
area of triangle
= 4 cm² ÷ 2 = 2 cm²

a.   b.

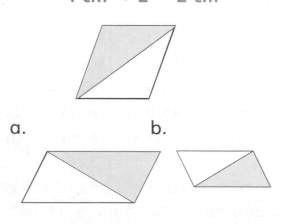

We already know how to calculate the area of any **right-angled triangle**.

We simply work out the area of the square or rectangle of which our triangle forms half, and then divide by 2:

We can write this as a RULE:

The area of a right-angled triangle = ($l \times b$) ÷ 2 unit²

But how can we measure the area of triangles which do not have a right angle, that is, obtuse-angled and acute-angled triangles?

The answer is simple: we divide our obtuse-angled or acute- angled triangle in such a way as to make two **right-angled triangles**:

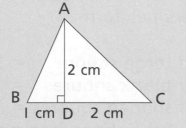

We calculate the area of each right-angled triangle, and add the two areas to find the total area of the original triangle: Example: Find the area of △ABC.

A

2 cm

B ⌐ C
1 cm D 2 cm

Area of △ABD = (2 cm × 1 cm) ÷ 2 = 1 cm²
Area of △ADC = (2 cm × 2 cm) ÷ 2 = 2 cm²
Area of △ABC = 1 cm² + 2 cm² = 3 cm²

Can you think of another way? What would happen if you place two identical triangles together?

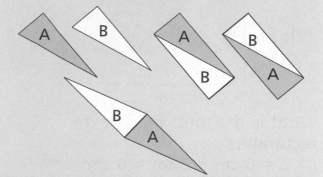

Triangles A and B are identical triangles, and have the same area.

You will need to flip triangle B to get a parallelogram. Now, find the area of the parallelogram, and divide it by 2 to get the area of the triangle.

▶ 9. Now, find the area of these triangles.

a.

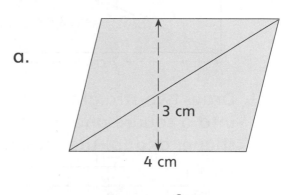

3 cm

4 cm

b.

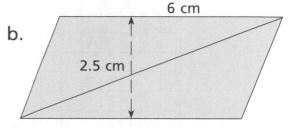

6 cm

2.5 cm

Area: More about Triangles

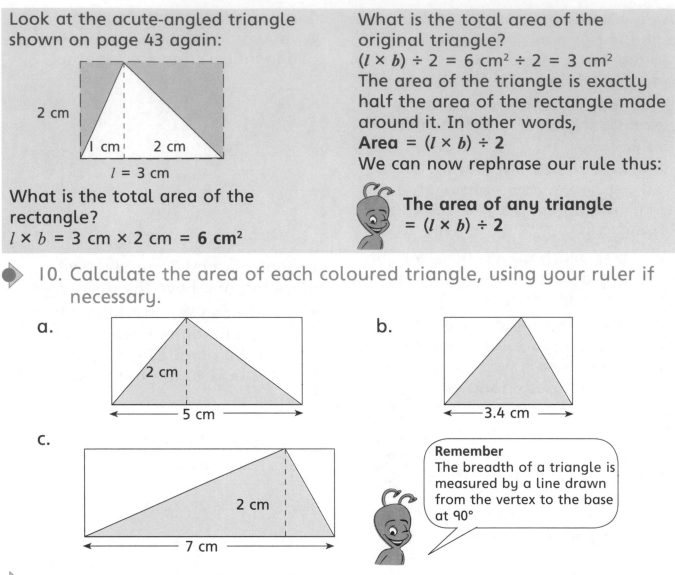

Look at the acute-angled triangle shown on page 43 again:

2 cm

1 cm | 2 cm

l = 3 cm

What is the total area of the rectangle?
$l \times b = 3 \text{ cm} \times 2 \text{ cm} = \textbf{6 cm}^2$

What is the total area of the original triangle?
$(l \times b) \div 2 = 6 \text{ cm}^2 \div 2 = 3 \text{ cm}^2$
The area of the triangle is exactly half the area of the rectangle made around it. In other words,
Area $= (l \times b) \div 2$
We can now rephrase our rule thus:

The area of any triangle
$= (l \times b) \div 2$

10. Calculate the area of each coloured triangle, using your ruler if necessary.

a.

2 cm

5 cm

b.

3.4 cm

c.

2 cm

7 cm

Remember
The breadth of a triangle is measured by a line drawn from the vertex to the base at 90°

11. Draw two straight lines from point A to divide the shaded area into a square and three triangles. Find (a) the total area of the shape, and (b) the area of the three shapes formed.

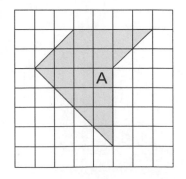

A

(a) Area of large square   = 64 cm²
    Area of blank squares   = _____
    Area of shaded squares = _____
(b) Now, cut the shape into a square and three triangles. Calculate area of each. Does it tally with (a)?

More about Shapes: Space and Volume

Area means the amount of **surface** a shape covers. For example, when we talk about the area of a house, we mean the amount of surface, or ground, it covers.

But in everyday life, we also need to know how much **space** an object takes up. For example, Sid needs to find out how many packets of cornflakes he can fit into his space larder:

To find out, Sid must calculate the amount of **space** available in the larder and the amount of **space** occupied by each packet of cornflakes.

The special word we use for 'the amount of space occupied' by an object is the **volume** of the object.

1. Look at these pairs of objects, then tick the object you think has the greater volume.

★

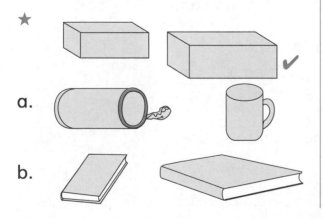

a.

b.

2. Look at these shapes made out of cube-shaped building blocks. Work out how many cubes have been used to make each shape.

★ **4 cubes**

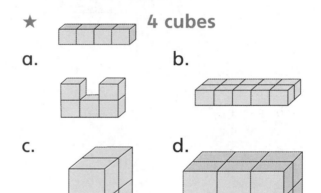

a.

b.

c.

d.

3. Do the two cuboids in each pair have the same volume? Write "yes" or "no".

★ 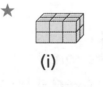 **No**
(i) = 12 cubes
(ii) = 18 cubes
(i)   (ii)

a. 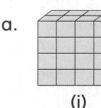 (i)   (ii)

b. 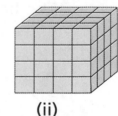 (i)   (ii)

OXFORD UNIVERSITY PRESS

Thinking about Volume

To help him understand the idea of **volume** more easily, Sid has made a cube out of paper. This is how he did it:

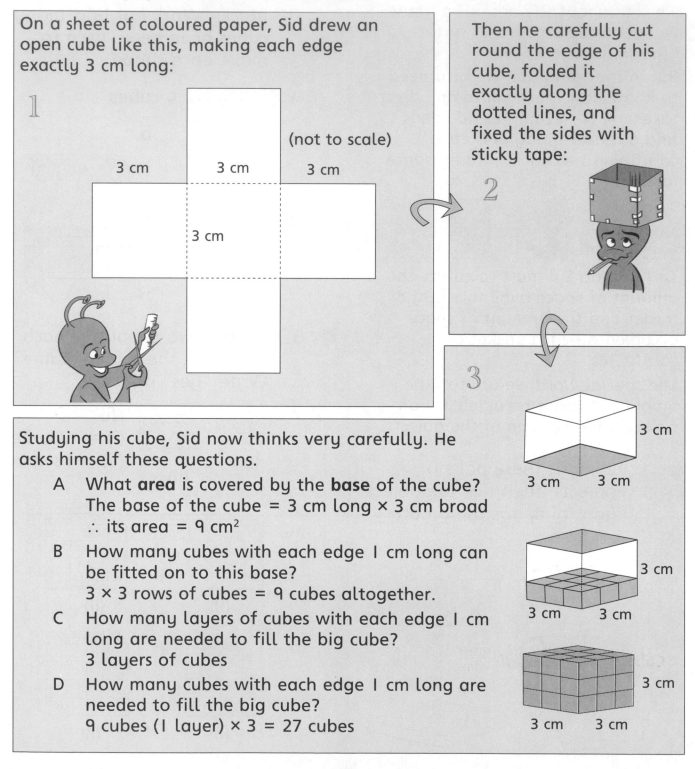

1 On a sheet of coloured paper, Sid drew an open cube like this, making each edge exactly 3 cm long:

(not to scale)

3 cm   3 cm   3 cm

3 cm

2 Then he carefully cut round the edge of his cube, folded it exactly along the dotted lines, and fixed the sides with sticky tape:

3

3 cm
3 cm   3 cm

3 cm
3 cm   3 cm

3 cm
3 cm   3 cm

Studying his cube, Sid now thinks very carefully. He asks himself these questions.

A   What **area** is covered by the **base** of the cube?
The base of the cube = 3 cm long × 3 cm broad
∴ its area = 9 cm²

B   How many cubes with each edge 1 cm long can be fitted on to this base?
3 × 3 rows of cubes = 9 cubes altogether.

C   How many layers of cubes with each edge 1 cm long are needed to fill the big cube?
3 layers of cubes

D   How many cubes with each edge 1 cm long are needed to fill the big cube?
9 cubes (1 layer) × 3 = 27 cubes

Volume: the Cubic Centimetre

1. Look at page 46 again. Look carefully at the open cube made by Sid. Now draw a cube of your own, making each edge 4 cm long.

   a. How many cubes with each edge of 1cm can be fitted on to the base of your cube?
   b. How many such layers are needed to fill the cube?

Note how Sid uses **multiplication** to help him find the number of small cubes that can be fitted into his empty cube:

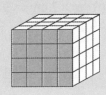

There are **16** cubes in each layer.
There are 4 layers.
∴ There are **64** cubes altogether.
16 × 4 = 64

2. Look at the cuboids below, then copy and complete the table.

3 × 2 × 3   4 × 3 × 3

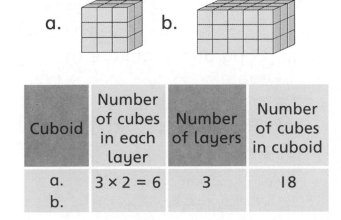

a.   b.

Cuboid	Number of cubes in each layer	Number of layers	Number of cubes in cuboid
a.	3 × 2 = 6	3	18
b.			

This cube has a volume of 1 cubic centimetre.
We say: **'One cubic centimetre'**.
We write: **1 cm³**
The little number '3' raised high to the right of 'cm' is a special symbol we use when we calculate volume.
Let us think why we use the number '3'. When we measure the length of a cube, we make just one measurement:

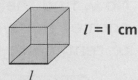

$l = 1$ cm

When we measure the area covered by a cube, we must make two measurements:

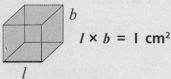

$l × b = 1$ cm²

But when we measure the volume of a cube, we make three measurements— the length, the breadth and the height (h):

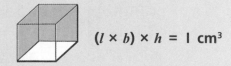

$(l × b) × h = 1$ cm³

3 is for three dimensions.
A cube is a 3-D object.

47

Volume: the Cubic Centimetre

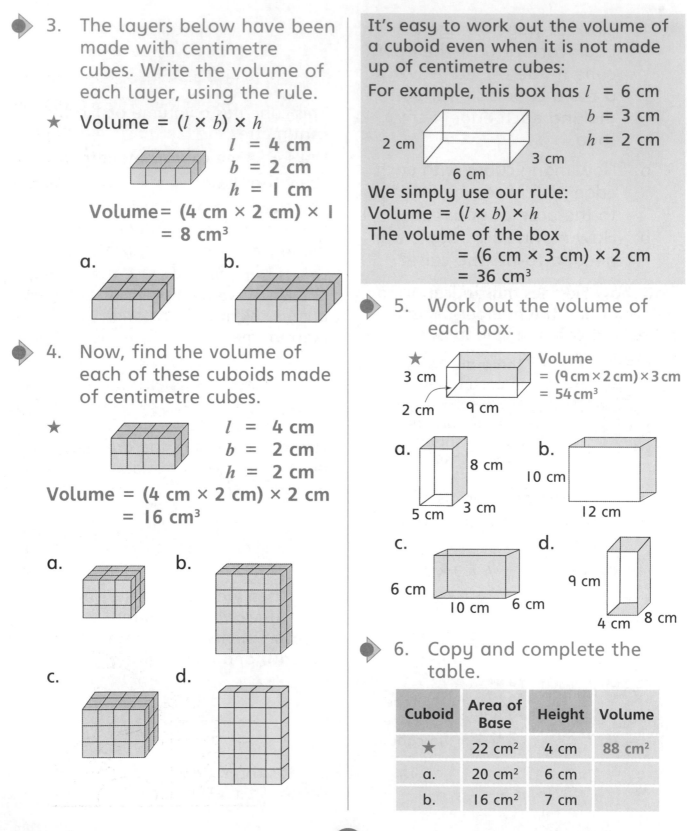

3. The layers below have been made with centimetre cubes. Write the volume of each layer, using the rule.

★ Volume = (l × b) × h

l = 4 cm
b = 2 cm
h = 1 cm

Volume = (4 cm × 2 cm) × 1
= 8 cm³

a.

b.

4. Now, find the volume of each of these cuboids made of centimetre cubes.

★
l = 4 cm
b = 2 cm
h = 2 cm

Volume = (4 cm × 2 cm) × 2 cm
= 16 cm³

a.

b.

c.

d.

It's easy to work out the volume of a cuboid even when it is not made up of centimetre cubes:
For example, this box has l = 6 cm
b = 3 cm
h = 2 cm

2 cm
3 cm
6 cm

We simply use our rule:
Volume = (l × b) × h
The volume of the box
= (6 cm × 3 cm) × 2 cm
= 36 cm³

5. Work out the volume of each box.

★
3 cm
2 cm
9 cm

Volume
= (9 cm × 2 cm) × 3 cm
= 54 cm³

a.
8 cm
5 cm
3 cm

b.
10 cm
12 cm

c.
6 cm
10 cm
6 cm

d.
9 cm
4 cm
8 cm

6. Copy and complete the table.

Cuboid	Area of Base	Height	Volume
★	22 cm²	4 cm	88 cm²
a.	20 cm²	6 cm	
b.	16 cm²	7 cm	

OXFORD
UNIVERSITY PRESS

7. Calculate the volume of cuboid each with these measurements.

   ★ $l = 12$ cm, $b = 4$ cm, $h = 3$ cm
   Volume = $(12 \text{ cm} \times 4 \text{ cm}) \times 3$ cm
   $= 48 \times 3 \text{ cm}^3 = 144 \text{ cm}^3$

   a. $l = 9$ cm, $b = 1.5$ cm, $h = 4$ cm
   b. $l = 6$ cm, $b = 2.5$ cm, $h = 8$ cm
   c. $l = 11$ cm, $b = 7$ cm, $h = 9$ cm

8. Look at these boxes. Sid knows the volume of each of them, but does not have one of the measurements. Help him find out the missing measurement by using division.

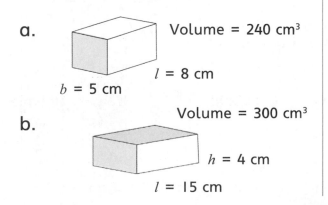

   ★ Volume = 216 cm³
   $b = 6$ cm
   $l = 9$ cm

   Volume = 216 cm³
   Area of base
   = 9 cm × 6 cm = 54 cm²
   ∴ Height = vol ÷ area
   $= 216 \text{ cm}^3 ÷ 54 \text{ cm}^2$
   $= 4$ cm

   a. Volume = 240 cm³
      $l = 8$ cm
      $b = 5$ cm

   b. Volume = 300 cm³
      $h = 4$ cm
      $l = 15$ cm

9. Now copy and complete this table.

Cuboid	length	Breadth	Height	Volume
★	9 cm	**8 cm**	5 cm	360 cm³
a.		12 cm	7 cm	924 cm³
b.	6 cm	6 cm		288 cm³
c.	11 cm		3 cm	396 cm³

10. Solve these word problems in your notebook, making complete statements.

   a. If a fish tank is 50 cm long, 20 cm wide and 15 cm high, how many cubic centimetres of water will it hold?

   b. Mandy Moon designs a classroom cupboard with a volume of 6 cubic metres (6 m³). If the cupboard is 3 m high and 1 m long, what is its breadth?

   c. The aquarium in Sid Spacewalker's home has a volume of 12,000 cm³. If it is 30 cm long and 20 cm wide, how high is it?

Rattle
Rattle

Fish food

OXFORD
UNIVERSITY PRESS

1 Sid Spacewalker remembers that when we measure the capacity of any container—for example a bottle or a cup or a bucket—we use litre (*l*) as the unit of measurement, and **millilitre** (*ml*) for very small capacities. But Sid also knows that we can measure **volume** by using **metre** (and **centimetre**) as the unit of measurement...

2 Sid decides to do an experiment. He first makes a cardboard cube with sides 10 cm long:

Its volume is (10 cm × 10 cm) × 10 cm = 1000 cm³.
Sid uses plenty of sticky tape to hold the cube together. He leaves the top of the cube open.

4 Sid discovers that the water from the bottle **completely** fills the cube, with none left over.
The capacity of Sid's 1 litre bottle is the **same** as the volume of his cube.

3 Sid next fills a 1 litre bottle with water. Very carefully, he empties the water from the bottle into his cube. (Because Sid has used plenty of sticky tape, very little water leaks out!)

5 Sid has discovered that **1000 cm³ = 1 litre = 1000 *ml***
From this, he understands that **1 cm³ = 1 *ml***

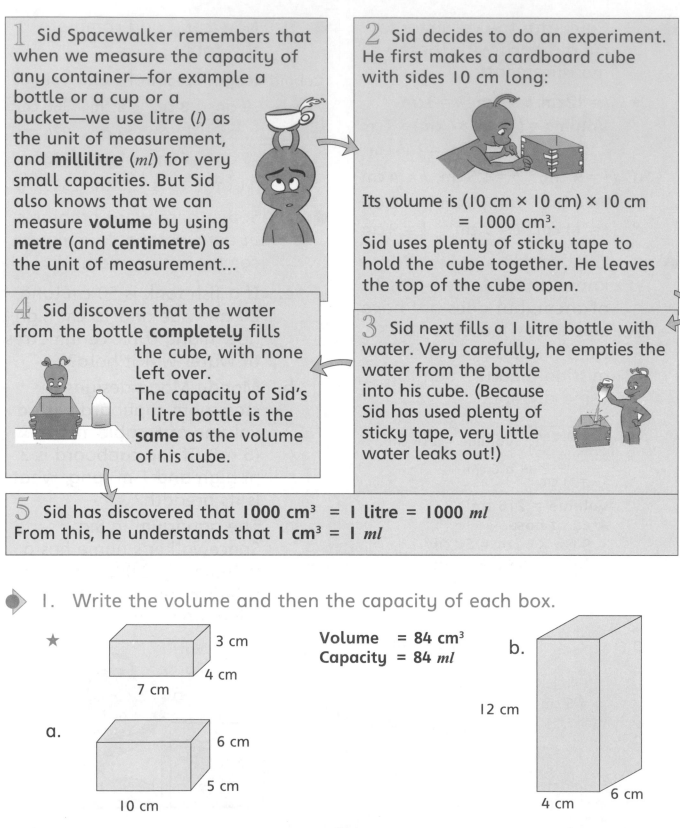

1. Write the volume and then the capacity of each box.

★

3 cm
4 cm
7 cm

Volume = 84 cm³
Capacity = 84 *ml*

b.

12 cm
4 cm
6 cm

a.

6 cm
5 cm
10 cm

1. Using graph paper, plot a line graph to show the number of children present at Modern School during a week in July 1991. Here is the data.

Children present	450	500	550	600	650
Day	Mon	Tue	Wed	Thu	Fri

2. Change these numbers into Pakistani periods.

   a. 124,900,938

   b. 51,670,324

3. Round off to the nearest 100.

   a. 15,550

   b. 84,472

4. Copy and complete.

   a. 384,691 ÷ 372

   b. 605,827 ÷ 453

5. Round off to the nearest cm.

   a. 16.5 cm

   b. 23.4 cm

6. Simplify these, using the DMAS rule.

   a. $8 \times 6 + 10 \div 2$

   b. $23 + 16 \div 4 \times 2$

   c. $48 \div 12 + 6 \times 4$

   d. $30 \div 6 \times 2 + 2$

7. Now simplify these.

   a. $(8.3 - 7.1) \times 9$

   b. $[90 - \{50 \div (30 \div 3)\}] - 28$

   c. $\left(\dfrac{5}{6} - \dfrac{1}{3}\right) + \left(\dfrac{4}{9} + \dfrac{2}{3}\right)$

   d. $4\dfrac{3}{4} - \left\{\dfrac{5}{8} + \left(3\dfrac{1}{4} - \dfrac{1}{2}\right)\right\}$

8. Calculate the area of each of these shapes.

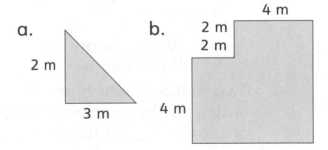

9. Calculate the volume of each of these boxes. Then give the capacity in *ml*.

   a. $l = 7\,cm, \quad b = 8.5\,cm, \; h = 6\,cm$

   b. $l = 10.5\,cm, \; b = 6\,cm, \quad h = 7\,cm$

   c. $l = 9.2\,cm, \; b = 7\,cm, \; h = 10\,cm$

OXFORD
UNIVERSITY PRESS

Remembering Multiples and Factors

★ Help Sid complete this review crossword.

Poison Weed
Factor Tree Killer

Sid's Little
Factor Tree

Clues—Across

1. 4, 6, 8, 10 and 12 are all _____ of the number 2.

4. Two numbers which have only 1 as their common factor are called _____ numbers.

6. All even numbers are multiples of this number.

7. Every number is a factor of _____ .

9. On a number line 1–10, the next greatest prime number after five is _____ .

10. The number eight has a total of _____ factors.

Clues—Down

2. A number with only two different factors (itself and 1) is called a _____ number.

3. _____ numbers have more than two different factors.

5. A multiple is a number which can be divided by another number without any _____ .

6. The LCM of 4 and 6 is _____ .

8. Number 1 is a _____ of every number.

9. 12, 48, 18 and 30 are all multiples of the number _____ .

1. Find the LCM of these pairs.

   10 and 15 ... 10 = 2 × 5

   15 = 3 × 5

   ★ LCM of 10 and 15 = 30

   a. 8, 12   b. 3, 7   c. 9, 15

2. Copy and complete the table.

1 ×	= 28
× 14	= 28
4 ×	= 28
7 ×	= 28

   Now write all the factors of 28.

3. How many factors does each number have?

   ★ 18 ... **6 factors (1, 2, 3, 6, 9, 18)**

   a. 24   b. 56   c. 75
   d. 25   e. 100   f. 91

4. By listing the factors of each number, find the HCF of these pairs.

   ★ 20, 25 ... 20: 1, 2, 4, 5 10, 20

   25: 1, 5, 25

   HCF of 20, 25 = 5

   a. 15, 39   b. 21, 17

5. Tick the pairs of co-prime numbers.

   ★ 5 and 11 ... 5 = 1 × 5,

   11 = 1 × 11

   a. 56 and 14   b. 100 and 25
   c. 23 and 29   d. 81 and 71

6. Are these statements true or false? Write T or F, explaining your answer.

   ★ 18 is a factor of 72 ... T (18 × 4 = 72)

   a. 15 and 35 are co-prime numbers.
   b. The HCF of 16 and 24 is 4.
   c. The LCM of 11 and 9 is 99.
   d. Among prime numbers, only the number 2 is an even number.
   e. 1030 is divisible by 3.
   f. 48,605 is divisible by 5.

7. Think carefully, then answer these.

   ★ Write a few pairs of numbers with HCF 7 ... 14 and 21; 28 and 49

   a. Write two 4–digit numbers divisible by 9.
   b. What is the smallest prime number?
   c. Draw factorization trees to show the prime factors of (a) 32 and (b) 45.
   d. If the LCM of a pair of numbers is 190 and one of the numbers is 10, what is the other number?

More Tests of Divisibility

In Book 4, we learnt four very useful **tests of divisibility**. They helped us find out, which factors make up a number.

 1. Sid Spacewalker is trying to remember his rules of divisibility.

Rule 67

Rule 37

Help him fill in the blanks.

a. Any number with 0 in the _____ column is divisible by 5.

b. An _____ number is always divisible by 2.

c. A number where digits add up to a multiple of 3 is divisible by _____ .

d. All numbers which are divisible by 9 have digits that add up to a multiple of _____ .

e. An example of a number which is divisible by 5 and by 10 is _____.

2. Which of these numbers is divisible by 3?

a. 149   b. 5481   c. 19,410

3. Which of these numbers is divisible by 5?

a. 16,495   b. 17,03,760   c. 705

4. Write down six 7-digit numbers which are divisible by 9.

Test 5: Multiples of 10
Look at these multiples of 10:
100; 17,100; 300,640; 7,032,790
They all have 0 in the ones column.

★ **Any number with 0 in the ones place is divisible by 10.**

5. Tick the numbers which are divisible by 10:

a. 4960   b. 5010   c. 720395

Test 6: Multiples of 4
Let's take the number 584, and look at the tens and ones digits:
5 (84)
Is 84 divisible by 4?
Yes, it is: 84 ÷ 4 = 21
And, all hundreds are divisible by 4
This tells us that 584, too, is divisible by 4. We can divide to check:

★ **A number is divisible by 4 if the number formed by the tens and ones digits can be divided by 4.**
584 ÷ 4 = 146 r 0

```
        146
    4)584
        4
       18
       16
       24
       24
      . . .
```

6. Which of these are divisible by 4?

a. 1996   b. 2000   c. 23,606

Test 7: Multiples of 6

Example: 918

1. We first ask ourselves 'is the number an even one?'
    The answer here is 'yes'.

2. Next we check whether the sum of the digits is divisible by 3:

    $$9 + 1 + 8 = 18$$

    Yes, it is.

So, the number 918 is divisible by both 2 and 3 (or 6).

Let us divide to check:

★ **A number is divisible by 6**
   (a) if it is even and
   (b) if the sum of its digits is divisible by 3.

```
      153
   6)918
      6
     31
     30
      18
      18
      ...
```

918 ÷ 6 = 153 r 0

7. Copy these numbers and see which of them are divisible by 6.

    a. 8622   b. 47,018

    c. 1463   d. 39,582

8. Look at these numbers carefully. Tick those which are divisible by 3 but not by 6.

    a. 4707   b. 801   c. 1,59,654

Test 8: Multiples of 8

One rule to remember is that **1000** is **always divisible by 8**. (Check this in your rough notebook.)

This means that all multiples of 1000 (2000, 3000, etc.) are also divisible by 8.

What happens if our number does not end with three zeros (i.e., not a multiple of 1000)?

Let us take the example 6128 and look at the digits in the hundreds, tens and ones:

   6 (128)

Is 128 (the number formed by the hundreds, tens and ones) divisible by 8?

Yes, it is: 128 ÷ 8 = 16

So, 6128, too, is divisible by 8.

We divide to check:

★ **A number with three zeros or a multiple of 8 in its hundreds, tens and units columns is divisible by 8.**

```
       766
   8)6128
      56
      52
      48
      48
      48
      ...
```

6128 ÷ 8 = 766 r 0

9. Check to see whether these numbers are divisible by 8.

    a. 4189   b. 1,17,000

    c. 6408   d. 1,493,600

Even more Tests of Divisibility

Sid has discovered **some more** short cuts. He has done this by applying the tests of divisibility he already knows:

Test 9: Multiples of 15

$$15 = 5 \times 3$$

Check to see if the given number is divisible by both 3 and 5.

Example 1605   – divisible by 5
                      – divisible by 3

So, 1605 is divisible by 15.

▶ 10. Check Test 9 on these numbers.

     a.   72,651   b. 300   c. 2532

Look at the numbers in the left-hand column of the table given below.

By which of the numbers along the top row is this number divisible?

Fill in all the boxes to complete this table:

Test 10: Multiples of 12

$$12 = 4 \times 3$$

Check to see if the given number is divisible by both 3 and 4.

Example 54,252 – divisible by 4
                        – divisible by 3

So, 54,252 is divisible by 12.

▶ 11. Check to see if these numbers are divisible by 12.

     a.   24,430   b. 1080   c. 81,156

Now play my Great Divisibility Game!

Divisible by	2	3	4	5	6	8	9	10	12
560	✓	×	✓	✓					
6100									
13,125				✓					
8000									
5,40,810									

In Book 4, we learnt how to break down numbers into **prime numbers** by simple division.

This helps us to find the LCM and HCF of larger numbers quickly and easily.

Let us find the prime factors of 72, using the division method.

72 is an even number, so we divide by 2 (2 is a prime number):

```
2 ) 72
2 ) 36     we divide by 2 again
2 ) 18     we divide by 2 again
3 ) 9      we divide by 3
3 ) 3      we divide by 3 again
  ) 1
```

The prime factors of 72 are **2** and **3**.

2 × 2 × 2 × 3 × 3 = 72

1. Find the prime factors of these numbers, using the division method. Then, check your answers.

   a. 156   b. 66   c. 475
   d. 212   e. 94   f. 164

2. Use brackets to help you.

   All the prime factors of 90 are given below.

   ★ **2 × 3 × 3 × 5 = (2 × 5) × (3 × 3)**
   = 10 × 9

   We have used groups of 10 to help us. Now, write the numbers with these factors:

   a. 2×2×5×5   b. 2×2×5×7
   c. 3×3×5   d. 2×2×3×3×5

   We already know that the **highest common factor** (HCF) of two or more numbers is the largest number which is a factor of all of them.

   For example, the HCF of 20 and 35 is 5.

   The HCF of 16, 24 and 32 is 8.

3. Write the HCF of:

   ★ 12, 16 and 20 ... HCF = 4
   a. 18, 27, 36   b. 12, 30
   c. 27, 54, 18   d. 38, 16, 14

The Division Method and HCF

Let's take two numbers: 56 and 140, and break them down into their prime factors:

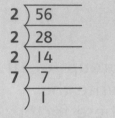

```
2 ) 56          2 ) 140
2 ) 28          2 ) 70
2 ) 14          5 ) 35
7 ) 7           7 ) 7
   ) 1             ) 1
```

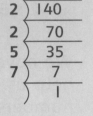

$56 = \boxed{2} \times \boxed{2} \times 2 \times \boxed{7}$

$140 = \boxed{2} \times \boxed{2} \times 5 \times \boxed{7}$

The HCF is the product of the factors common to both.

What are the common factors here?

The common factors are 2, 2 and 7.

So the HCF $= 2 \times 2 \times 7$
$\qquad\qquad = 28$

LCM = **HCF × all other factors**
$\qquad$ = **28 × 2 × 5 = 280**

4. Break these pairs of numbers into their prime factors, then find their HCF and LCM.

   a. 64 and 148   b. 63 and 108

   c. 26 and 96   d. 27 and 130

5. These are numbers that have already been broken down into their prime factors. Quickly find the HCF of each pair.

   ★ $2\times3\times7\times5$ and $2\times5\times2$
      CF = 2 and 5
      ∴ HCF = 2×5 = 10

   a. $2\times2\times2\times5$ and $2\times2\times3\times5$

   b. $2\times3\times3\times5$ and $2\times3\times5\times7$

   c. $2\times3\times5\times5$ and $3\times5\times5\times7$

6. Now find the HCF of each set of three or more numbers.

Remember: the HCF is the product of the common factors

   ★ $2 \times 2 \times 3$; $2 \times 3 \times 3$; and $2 \times 3 \times 3$
      Common factors = $\boxed{2} \times 2 \times \boxed{3}$
      $\qquad\qquad\qquad\quad \boxed{2} \times 3 \times 3$
      $\qquad\qquad\qquad\quad \boxed{2} \times \boxed{3} \times 3$

   ∴ HCF = 2×3 = 6

   a. $2 \times 3 \times 3$; $2 \times 2 \times 2$; and $2 \times 2 \times 3$

   b. $2 \times 2 \times 3 \times 5$; $2 \times 2 \times 5$ and $2 \times 3 \times 3 \times 5$

OXFORD
UNIVERSITY PRESS

The HCF of Larger Numbers

By breaking large numbers into their prime factors and then finding the common factors, it is easy to work out the HCF of larger numbers.

Let us try it with 3 big numbers:
70, 98 and 154

```
2)70        2)98        2)154
5)35        7)49        7)77
7) 7        7) 7       11) 11
   1           1           1
```

What are the common factors?

70 = 2 × 5 × 7
98 = 2 × 7 × 7
154 = 2 × 7 × 11

∴ HCF of 70, 98 and 154 = 2 × 7 = 14
LCM of 70, 98 and 154 = 14 × 5 ×
                              7 × 11
                       = 5390

1. Find the HCF and LCM of:

a. 132 and 220

b. 180 and 252

c. 120 and 168

d. 175, 300 and 425

e. 70, 147 and 98

What do we do when we want to find the HCF of two much larger numbers, for example, 1271 and 1681?

If we try to use the **division method**, we run into a problem: neither of our two numbers is divisible by 2, 3, 5, 7, 11 or 13.

Sid has discovered a magical method based on **long division**.

Sid first makes the bigger number his dividend and the smaller number his divisor. Then he divides:

```
              1
       1271)1681
            1271
```
Sid's remainder = 410

Next, Sid changes his remainder into a divisor, and his old divisor into a dividend.

```
              3
        410)1271
            1230
```
His remainder = 41

Next, he does the trick again! The remainder becomes the divisor, the old divisor becomes the dividend!

```
             10
         41)410
            410
              0
```

Sid can't do his trick again, because he has no remainder.
So he knows that the **HCF of 1271 and 1681 = 41**
This method does not give you an immediate LCM.

OXFORD
UNIVERSITY PRESS

The HCF of Larger Numbers: Long Division Method

When Sid finds the HCF of 2 or more large numbers using the long division method, he works diagonally across his notebook, quietly saying aloud to himself each stage of this sum, just like a magic spell.

1 Make the bigger number the dividend, make the smaller number the divisor, then divide:

2 Make your remainder the new divisor, change your old divisor into the dividend, then

3 Repeat stage 2:

4 Repeat stage 2:

5 Repeat!

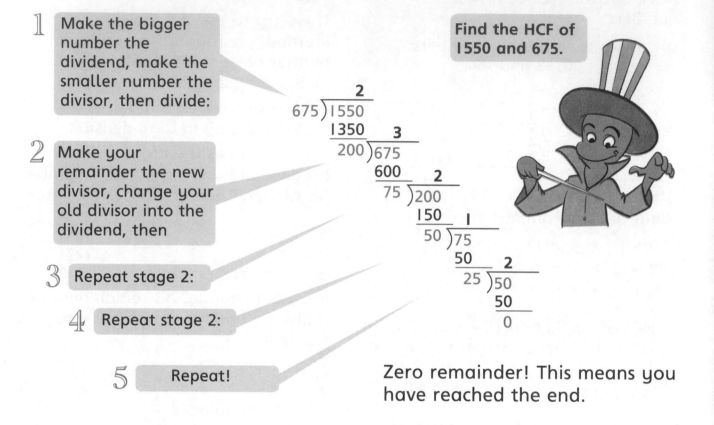

Find the HCF of 1550 and 675.

$$675 \overline{)1550} \quad 2$$
$$\underline{1350}$$
$$200\overline{)675} \quad 3$$
$$\underline{600}$$
$$75\overline{)200} \quad 2$$
$$\underline{150}$$
$$50\overline{)75} \quad 1$$
$$\underline{50}$$
$$25\overline{)50} \quad 2$$
$$\underline{50}$$
$$0$$

Zero remainder! This means you have reached the end.

The HCF of 1550 and 675 is 25.

2. Use Sid's method to find the HCF of these pairs.
   a. 105;93   b. 272;1278
   c. 999;851   d. 513;405

3. Now find the HCF and LCM of these pairs.
   a. 1100;1490   b. 722;1406
   c. 1272;901   d. 2272;1278

The Division Method and LCM

When we break numbers down into their prime factors, using the **division method**, it is easy to find their lowest common multiple (LCM).

Let us take **12** and **18** and find their prime factors:

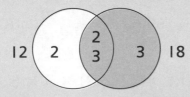

```
2 ) 12        2 ) 18
2 ) 6         3 ) 9
3 ) 3         3 ) 3
    1             1
```

Using a Venn diagram, we can show their prime factors thus:

12 (2 (2 3) 3) 18

HCF of 12 and 18 = 6

The LCM of the two numbers must include all the prime factors of each of them. We find the LCM by multiplying together all the prime factors. But we include the common factors only once:

LCM of 12 and 18 = (2 × 3) × 2 × 3
= 36

Remember: The LCM of two numbers is the product of their HCF and all other prime factors.

1. Using the division method, find the LCM of these pairs.
   a. 42;126   b. 20;56

2. These pairs of numbers are broken down into their prime factors. Quickly find the LCM of each pair.
   ★ 2 × 2 × 3 and 2 × 2 × 5
   LCM = (2 × 2) × 3 × 5 = 60
   a. 2 × 2 × 3 and 2 × 7
   b. 2 × 2 × 2 and 2 × 2 × 3
   c. 2 × 2 × 5 and 5 ×5

3. Look at the pairs of numbers in Exercise 2 above. As quickly as you can, change the numbers back into whole numbers.
   ★ 2 × 2 × 3 and 2 × 2 × 5
              12 and 20

4. Match each pair of numbers shown on the left to the correct LCM (use your rough notebook to make your calculations).
   a. 16 and 12
   b. 27 and 45
   c. 36 and 24
   d. 55 and 66
   e. 40 and 32
   f. 15 and 125
   g. 70 and 98
   h. 30 and 40

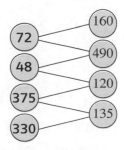

OXFORD
UNIVERSITY PRESS

LCM of Three Numbers

Suppose we want to find the LCM of a set of three numbers.

We follow exactly the same steps.

Let us take the set 12, 18 and 27.

First, we break each number down into its prime factors:

2) 12	2) 18	3) 27
2) 6	3) 9	3) 9
3) 3	3) 3	3) 3
) 1	) 1	) 1

We then list the prime factors and loop together the common factors:

$$12 = 2 \times 2 \times 3$$
$$18 = 2 \times 3 \times 3$$
$$27 = 3 \times 3 \times 3$$

LCM $= 3 \times 2 \times 2 \times 3 \times 3 = 108$

We can check by drawing a Venn diagram:

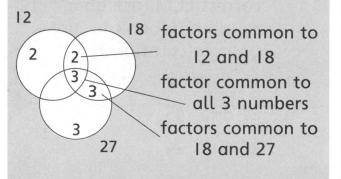

12

18 factors common to 12 and 18

factor common to all 3 numbers

factors common to 18 and 27

27

LCM $= 2 \times 2 \times 3 \times 3 \times 3$
$= 4 \times 9 \times 3$
$= 108$

The LCM of 12, 18 and 27 = 108

Find the HCF of 12, 18 and 27.

The HCF of 12, 18 and 27 = 3

1. Find the LCM of these sets of numbers.
   a. 6, 9 and 15
   b. 10, 12 and 20
   c. 12, 15 and 18

2. Using a coin, draw Venn diagrams to show the prime factors and common prime factors of these pairs of numbers. Then work out the LCM.

   ★ $2 \times 2 \times 3 \times 5$ and $2 \times 3 \times 3$

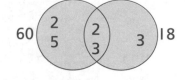

   LCM $= (2 \times 3) \times 3 \times 5 \times 2$
   $= 180$

   a. $2 \times 3 \times 5$ and $2 \times 2 \times 5$
   b. $2 \times 2 \times 2 \times 3$ and $2 \times 2 \times 3$

3. Repeat Exercise 2, this time with three numbers and three circles.

   ★ $2 \times 2 \times 2$; 2×3; $2 \times 3 \times 3$

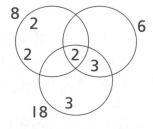

   LCM $= 2 \times 2 \times 2 \times 3 \times 3 = 72$

   a. 2×2; 2×3; 2×5
   b. $2 \times 2 \times 2$; 2×5; $2 \times 3 \times 5$

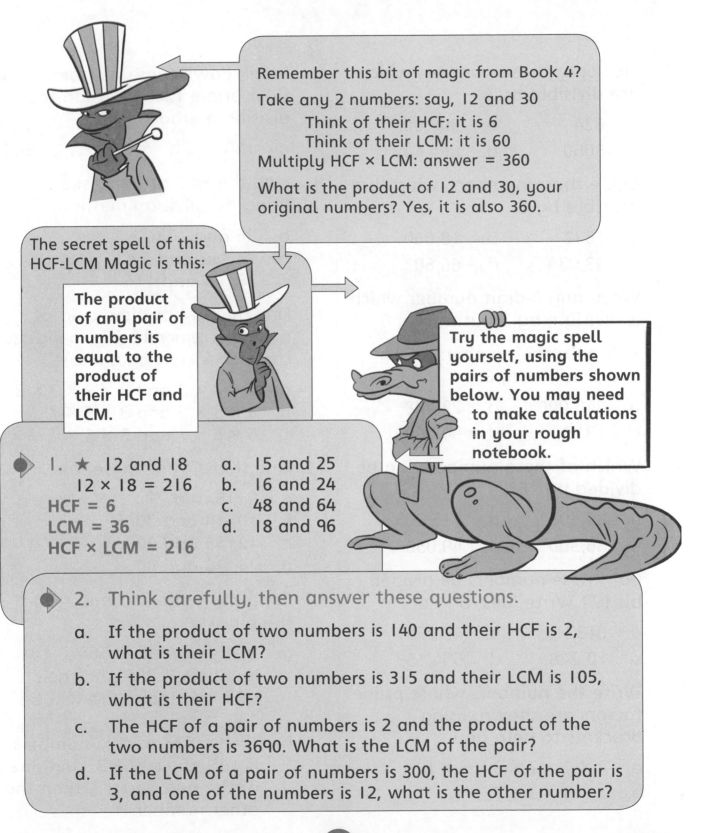

Remember this bit of magic from Book 4?

Take any 2 numbers: say, 12 and 30
   Think of their HCF: it is 6
   Think of their LCM: it is 60
Multiply HCF × LCM: answer = 360

What is the product of 12 and 30, your original numbers? Yes, it is also 360.

The secret spell of this HCF-LCM Magic is this:

The product of any pair of numbers is equal to the product of their HCF and LCM.

Try the magic spell yourself, using the pairs of numbers shown below. You may need to make calculations in your rough notebook.

1. ★ 12 and 18
   12 × 18 = 216
   HCF = 6
   LCM = 36
   HCF × LCM = 216

   a. 15 and 25
   b. 16 and 24
   c. 48 and 64
   d. 18 and 96

2. Think carefully, then answer these questions.

   a. If the product of two numbers is 140 and their HCF is 2, what is their LCM?

   b. If the product of two numbers is 315 and their LCM is 105, what is their HCF?

   c. The HCF of a pair of numbers is 2 and the product of the two numbers is 3690. What is the LCM of the pair?

   d. If the LCM of a pair of numbers is 300, the HCF of the pair is 3, and one of the numbers is 12, what is the other number?

1. Tick only those numbers which are divisible by 4.

    a. 624　　　　b. 308,005
    c. 3060　　　d. 864,442

2. Circle those numbers, which are divisible by 6.

    a. 1572　　　b. 18,060
    c. 43,034　　d. 66,603

3. Write any 4-digit number which is divisible by 3 but not by 6.

4. Tick only the numbers which are divisible by 8.

    a. 846,000　　b. 22,408
    c. 1318　　　d. 903,000

5. Which of these numbers can be divided by 15?

    a. 80,505　　b. 215,205
    c. 86,300　　d. 49,050

6. Can these numbers be divided by 12? Write 'yes' or 'no'.

    a. 8132　　　b. 45,265
    c. 10,248　　d. 594,156

7. Write the numbers whose prime factors are shown, using brackets to help you.

    a. $2 \times 2 \times 2 \times 3 \times 3 \times 5$
    b. $2 \times 3 \times 3 \times 7$

8. Break down these numbers into their prime factors, using the division method.

    a. 148　　b. 210　c. 365

9. Find the HCF of these sets, using the division method.

    a. 36 and 108
    b. 24,112 and 72
    c. 38, 95 and 114

10. Find the LCM of these pairs of numbers, remembering to include common factors only once.

    a. $2 \times 2 \times 3$ and $2 \times 2 \times 2 \times 3$
    b. $3 \times 3 \times 5$ and $3 \times 5 \times 7$
    c. $5 \times 5 \times 7$ and $2 \times 5 \times 7$

11. Find the LCM of these sets.

    a. 9, 18 and 21
    b. 10, 14 and 30
    c. 12, 16 and 20
    d. 24, 30 and 40

12. Copy the sentences and fill in the blanks.

    a. If the product of two numbers is 756 and their HCF is 6, their LCM will be _____

    b. If the LCM of two numbers is 105, their HCF 3, and one of the numbers 15, then the other number is _____

Fabulous Fraction Fun-Fair

Sid, Sara, Sue, Selvi and Sprog are enjoying a day out at the Fabulous Fraction Fun-Fair. Help them win lots of prizes by solving the fraction puzzles set at each stall. Copy the sums in your notebook and complete.

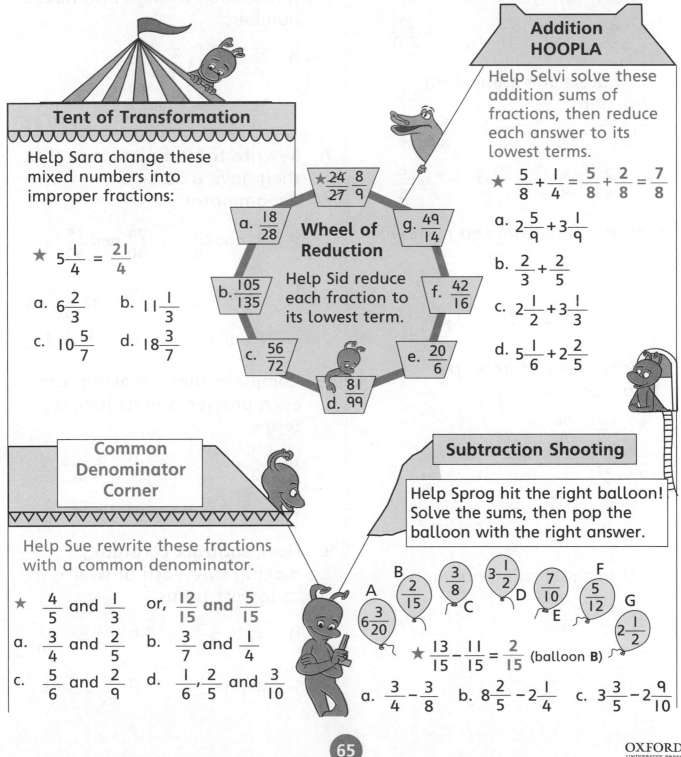

Tent of Transformation

Help Sara change these mixed numbers into improper fractions:

★ $5\frac{1}{4} = \frac{21}{4}$

a. $6\frac{2}{3}$ b. $11\frac{1}{3}$

c. $10\frac{5}{7}$ d. $18\frac{3}{7}$

Wheel of Reduction

Help Sid reduce each fraction to its lowest term.

★ $\frac{24}{27}$ $\frac{8}{9}$

a. $\frac{18}{28}$

g. $\frac{49}{14}$

b. $\frac{105}{135}$

f. $\frac{42}{16}$

c. $\frac{56}{72}$

d. $\frac{81}{99}$

e. $\frac{20}{6}$

Addition HOOPLA

Help Selvi solve these addition sums of fractions, then reduce each answer to its lowest terms.

★ $\frac{5}{8} + \frac{1}{4} = \frac{5}{8} + \frac{2}{8} = \frac{7}{8}$

a. $2\frac{5}{9} + 3\frac{1}{9}$

b. $\frac{2}{3} + \frac{2}{5}$

c. $2\frac{1}{2} + 3\frac{1}{3}$

d. $5\frac{1}{6} + 2\frac{2}{5}$

Common Denominator Corner

Help Sue rewrite these fractions with a common denominator.

★ $\frac{4}{5}$ and $\frac{1}{3}$ or, $\frac{12}{15}$ and $\frac{5}{15}$

a. $\frac{3}{4}$ and $\frac{2}{5}$ b. $\frac{3}{7}$ and $\frac{1}{4}$

c. $\frac{5}{6}$ and $\frac{2}{9}$ d. $\frac{1}{6}, \frac{2}{5}$ and $\frac{3}{10}$

Subtraction Shooting

Help Sprog hit the right balloon! Solve the sums, then pop the balloon with the right answer.

A $6\frac{3}{20}$ B $\frac{2}{15}$ $\frac{3}{8}$ C $3\frac{1}{2}$ D $\frac{7}{10}$ E   F $\frac{5}{12}$ G $2\frac{1}{2}$

★ $\frac{13}{15} - \frac{11}{15} = \frac{2}{15}$ (balloon B)

a. $\frac{3}{4} - \frac{3}{8}$ b. $8\frac{2}{5} - 2\frac{1}{4}$ c. $3\frac{3}{5} - 2\frac{9}{10}$

OXFORD
UNIVERSITY PRESS

More Fractions

1. Reduce these fractions to their lowest terms.

   a. $\dfrac{25}{55}$ b. $\dfrac{72}{81}$ c. $\dfrac{27}{270}$

2. Complete the equivalent fractions.

   a. $\dfrac{4}{7} = \dfrac{*}{35}$ b. $\dfrac{64}{88} = \dfrac{8}{*}$

   c. $\dfrac{25}{40} = \dfrac{*}{8}$ d. $\dfrac{*}{42} = \dfrac{5}{6}$

3. Write these as mixed numbers.

   ★ $\dfrac{19}{4} = 4\dfrac{3}{4}$

   a. $\dfrac{25}{3}$ b. $\dfrac{61}{8}$ c. $\dfrac{77}{10}$

4. Write these as improper fractions.

   ★ $6\dfrac{2}{9} = \dfrac{56}{9}$

   a. $5\dfrac{11}{12}$ b. $7\dfrac{2}{7}$

   c. $10\dfrac{2}{5}$ d. $12\dfrac{6}{7}$

5. Fill in the missing numbers.

   a. $\dfrac{7}{8} = \dfrac{}{96}$

   b. $\dfrac{8}{9} = \dfrac{112}{}$

   c. $\dfrac{72}{96} = \underline{\qquad}$

6. Reduce these to their lowest terms, then change into mixed numbers.

   ★ $\dfrac{55}{45} = \dfrac{11}{9} = 1\dfrac{2}{9}$

   a. $\dfrac{38}{16}$ b. $\dfrac{44}{24}$ c. $\dfrac{110}{60}$

7. Rewrite these fractions so that they have a common denominator.

   ★ $\dfrac{3}{5}$ and $\dfrac{3}{8}$ ... $\dfrac{24}{40}$ and $\dfrac{15}{40}$

   a. $\dfrac{2}{7}$ and $\dfrac{3}{14}$ b. $\dfrac{21}{32}$ and $\dfrac{3}{8}$

   c. $\dfrac{5}{8}$ and $\dfrac{3}{20}$ d. $\dfrac{3}{4}$ and $\dfrac{9}{10}$

8. Complete these, making sure each answer is in its lowest terms.

   a. $\dfrac{2}{5} + \dfrac{1}{4}$ b. $5\dfrac{3}{4} + 2\dfrac{5}{6}$

   c. $1\dfrac{5}{6} + \dfrac{2}{5}$ d. $2\dfrac{5}{6} + \dfrac{2}{2}$

9. Now, subtract carefully, making sure each answer is in its lowest terms.

   a. $5\dfrac{1}{2} - 3\dfrac{3}{8}$ b. $7\dfrac{2}{3} - 3\dfrac{3}{10}$

   c. $8\dfrac{1}{3} - 4\dfrac{1}{9}$ d. $12\dfrac{2}{5} - 6\dfrac{7}{8}$

Multiplication of Fractions: First Ideas

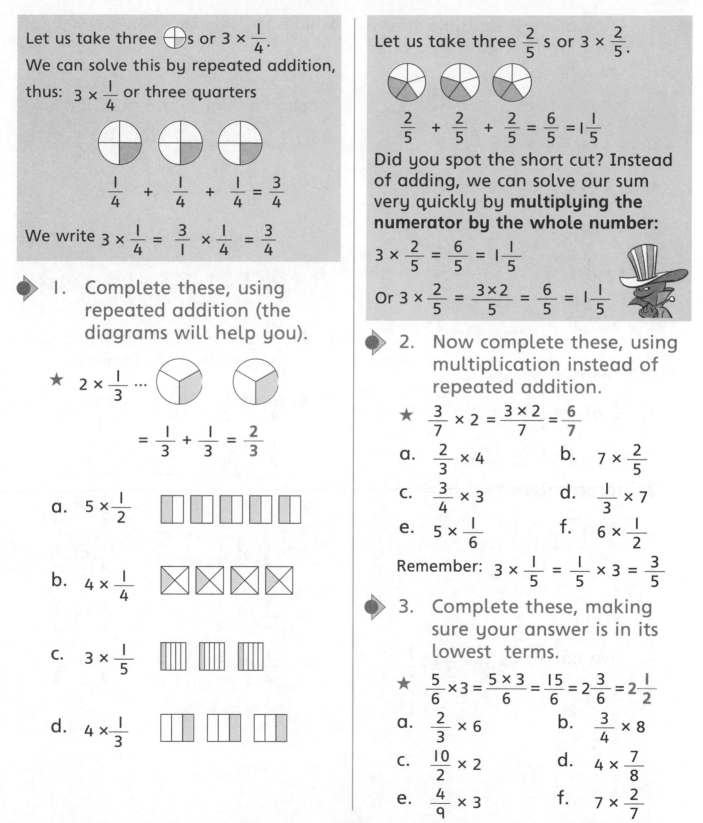

Let us take three ⊕s or $3 \times \frac{1}{4}$.
We can solve this by repeated addition, thus: $3 \times \frac{1}{4}$ or three quarters

$$\frac{1}{4} + \frac{1}{4} + \frac{1}{4} = \frac{3}{4}$$

We write $3 \times \frac{1}{4} = \frac{3}{1} \times \frac{1}{4} = \frac{3}{4}$

Let us take three $\frac{2}{5}$ s or $3 \times \frac{2}{5}$.

$$\frac{2}{5} + \frac{2}{5} + \frac{2}{5} = \frac{6}{5} = 1\frac{1}{5}$$

Did you spot the short cut? Instead of adding, we can solve our sum very quickly by **multiplying the numerator by the whole number:**

$$3 \times \frac{2}{5} = \frac{6}{5} = 1\frac{1}{5}$$

Or $3 \times \frac{2}{5} = \frac{3 \times 2}{5} = \frac{6}{5} = 1\frac{1}{5}$

1. Complete these, using repeated addition (the diagrams will help you).

★ $2 \times \frac{1}{3}$ ...

$= \frac{1}{3} + \frac{1}{3} = \frac{2}{3}$

a. $5 \times \frac{1}{2}$

b. $4 \times \frac{1}{4}$

c. $3 \times \frac{1}{5}$

d. $4 \times \frac{1}{3}$

2. Now complete these, using multiplication instead of repeated addition.

★ $\frac{3}{7} \times 2 = \frac{3 \times 2}{7} = \frac{6}{7}$

a. $\frac{2}{3} \times 4$ b. $7 \times \frac{2}{5}$

c. $\frac{3}{4} \times 3$ d. $\frac{1}{3} \times 7$

e. $5 \times \frac{1}{6}$ f. $6 \times \frac{1}{2}$

Remember: $3 \times \frac{1}{5} = \frac{1}{5} \times 3 = \frac{3}{5}$

3. Complete these, making sure your answer is in its lowest terms.

★ $\frac{5}{6} \times 3 = \frac{5 \times 3}{6} = \frac{15}{6} = 2\frac{3}{6} = 2\frac{1}{2}$

a. $\frac{2}{3} \times 6$ b. $\frac{3}{4} \times 8$

c. $\frac{10}{2} \times 2$ d. $4 \times \frac{7}{8}$

e. $\frac{4}{9} \times 3$ f. $7 \times \frac{2}{7}$

OXFORD
UNIVERSITY PRESS

Multiplying a Fraction by a Fraction

1. Look at these multiplications. Copy and complete them in your notebook.

a. $\dfrac{1}{2} \times 4 = \dfrac{1}{2} \times \dfrac{4}{1} = \dfrac{4}{2} = 2$

b. $3 \times \dfrac{1}{2} =$

c. $\dfrac{1}{2} \times 2 =$

d. $5 \times \dfrac{1}{2} =$

e. $\dfrac{1}{2} \times \dfrac{1}{2} =$

Look at these;

1. $\dfrac{1}{2}$ of $4 = \dfrac{1}{2} \times 4 = 2$

△ △/△ △

2. three halves $3 \times \dfrac{1}{2} = \dfrac{3}{2} = 1\dfrac{1}{2}$

3. $\dfrac{1}{2}$ of $2 = \dfrac{1}{2} \times 2 = 1$

⬡/⬡

4. five halves $5 \times \dfrac{1}{2} = \dfrac{5}{2} = 2\dfrac{1}{2}$

5. $\dfrac{1}{2}$ of $\dfrac{1}{2}$

$= \dfrac{1}{2} \times \dfrac{1}{2}$

$= \dfrac{1}{4}$

What is the difference between

(a) $\dfrac{1}{2} \times \dfrac{1}{3}$ and   (b) $\dfrac{1}{3} \times \dfrac{1}{2}$?

= half of a third   = a third of a half

(a) $\dfrac{1}{2} \times \dfrac{1}{3}$

$= \dfrac{1}{6}$

(b) $\dfrac{1}{3} \times \dfrac{1}{2}$

$= \dfrac{1}{6}$

Both are the same.

So, $\dfrac{1}{2} \times \dfrac{1}{3} = \dfrac{1}{3} \times \dfrac{1}{2} = \dfrac{1}{6}$

2. Draw pairs of diagrams to show these statements.

★ $\dfrac{1}{4}$ of $\dfrac{1}{2}$

$\dfrac{1}{2}$ of $\dfrac{1}{4}$

a. $\dfrac{1}{5}$ of $\dfrac{1}{2}$

$\dfrac{1}{2}$ of $\dfrac{1}{5}$

b. $\dfrac{1}{2}$ of $\dfrac{1}{3}$

$\dfrac{1}{3}$ of $\dfrac{1}{2}$

c. $\dfrac{3}{4}$ of $\dfrac{1}{2}$

$\dfrac{1}{2}$ of $\dfrac{3}{4}$

d. $\dfrac{1}{2}$ of $\dfrac{2}{3}$

$\dfrac{2}{3}$ of $\dfrac{1}{2}$

3. Write statements to match these diagrams.

$\frac{1}{3}$ $\frac{1}{2}$ of $\frac{1}{3}$

a.

b.

4. Now draw diagrams to match these multiplications, and write the product of each.

★ $\frac{1}{3} \times \frac{1}{2}$

$\frac{1}{2}$ $\frac{1}{3} \times \frac{1}{2} = \frac{1}{6}$

a. $\frac{1}{2} \times \frac{3}{4}$ b. $\frac{1}{4} \times \frac{2}{5}$

c. $\frac{1}{3} \times \frac{1}{4}$ d. $\frac{2}{3} \times \frac{1}{4}$

Look carefully at the results you have written for Exercise 4.

Do you notice a pattern? For example:

$\frac{3}{4}$ $\frac{1}{2} \times \frac{3}{4}$

We can find the answer by multiplying thus:

$\frac{1 \times 3}{2 \times 4} = \frac{3}{8}$

5. Use multiplication to find the products, then draw diagrams to check.

★ $\frac{3}{4} \times \frac{1}{6} \dots \frac{3 \times 1}{4 \times 6} = \frac{3}{24} = \frac{1}{8}$

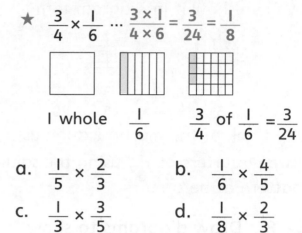

I whole $\frac{1}{6}$ $\frac{3}{4}$ of $\frac{1}{6} = \frac{3}{24}$

a. $\frac{1}{5} \times \frac{2}{3}$ b. $\frac{1}{6} \times \frac{4}{5}$

c. $\frac{1}{3} \times \frac{3}{5}$ d. $\frac{1}{8} \times \frac{2}{3}$

6. Now find the products of these, using multiplication only.

★ $\frac{1}{10} \times \frac{4}{7} \dots \frac{1 \times 4}{10 \times 7} = \frac{4}{70}$

a. $\frac{1}{9} \times \frac{2}{3}$ b. $\frac{1}{5} \times \frac{7}{8}$

c. $\frac{1}{8} \times \frac{5}{6}$ d. $\frac{3}{4} \times \frac{5}{12}$

e. $\frac{1}{11} \times \frac{3}{4}$ f. $\frac{1}{5} \times \frac{7}{8}$

7. Solve these multiplications.

a. $\frac{1}{12} \times \frac{4}{7}$ b. $\frac{1}{5} \times \frac{4}{7}$

c. $\frac{1}{10} \times \frac{5}{9}$ d. $\frac{1}{9} \times \frac{9}{11}$

e. $\frac{1}{6} \times \frac{9}{10}$ f. $\frac{1}{6} \times \frac{7}{11}$

g. $\frac{1}{14} \times \frac{3}{4}$ h. $\frac{1}{12} \times \frac{5}{9}$

OXFORD
UNIVERSITY PRESS

Multiplying a Fraction by a Fraction

Look carefully at this multiplication:

$$\frac{3}{4} \times \frac{3}{5}$$

We can show it in diagram form:

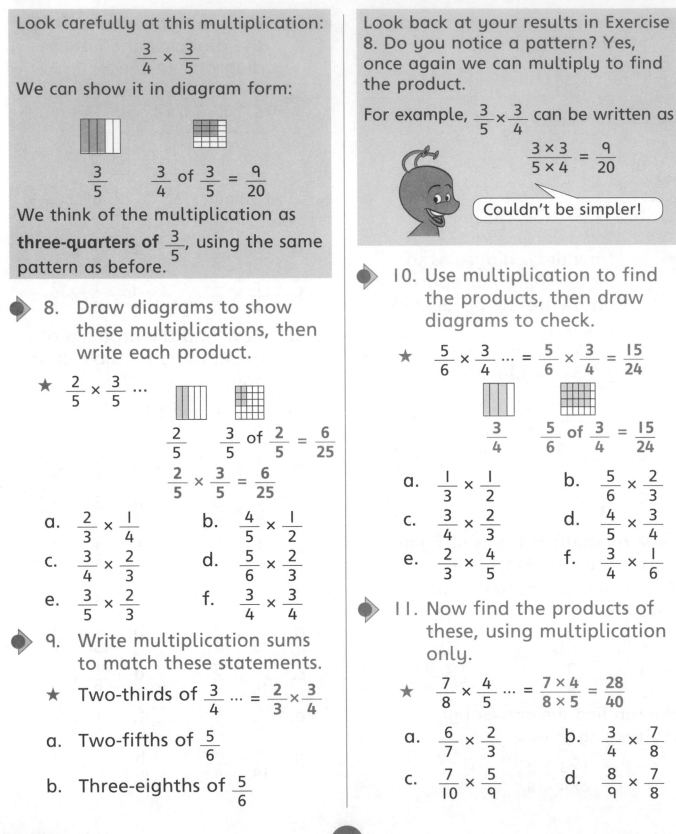

$$\frac{3}{5} \qquad \frac{3}{4} \text{ of } \frac{3}{5} = \frac{9}{20}$$

We think of the multiplication as **three-quarters of** $\frac{3}{5}$, using the same pattern as before.

8. Draw diagrams to show these multiplications, then write each product.

★ $\frac{2}{5} \times \frac{3}{5}$ ...

$$\frac{2}{5} \qquad \frac{3}{5} \text{ of } \frac{2}{5} = \frac{6}{25}$$

$$\frac{2}{5} \times \frac{3}{5} = \frac{6}{25}$$

a. $\frac{2}{3} \times \frac{1}{4}$ b. $\frac{4}{5} \times \frac{1}{2}$

c. $\frac{3}{4} \times \frac{2}{3}$ d. $\frac{5}{6} \times \frac{2}{3}$

e. $\frac{3}{5} \times \frac{2}{3}$ f. $\frac{3}{4} \times \frac{3}{4}$

9. Write multiplication sums to match these statements.

★ Two-thirds of $\frac{3}{4}$ ... $= \frac{2}{3} \times \frac{3}{4}$

a. Two-fifths of $\frac{5}{6}$

b. Three-eighths of $\frac{5}{6}$

Look back at your results in Exercise 8. Do you notice a pattern? Yes, once again we can multiply to find the product.

For example, $\frac{3}{5} \times \frac{3}{4}$ can be written as

$$\frac{3 \times 3}{5 \times 4} = \frac{9}{20}$$

Couldn't be simpler!

10. Use multiplication to find the products, then draw diagrams to check.

★ $\frac{5}{6} \times \frac{3}{4}$ ... $= \frac{5}{6} \times \frac{3}{4} = \frac{15}{24}$

$$\frac{3}{4} \qquad \frac{5}{6} \text{ of } \frac{3}{4} = \frac{15}{24}$$

a. $\frac{1}{3} \times \frac{1}{2}$ b. $\frac{5}{6} \times \frac{2}{3}$

c. $\frac{3}{4} \times \frac{2}{3}$ d. $\frac{4}{5} \times \frac{3}{4}$

e. $\frac{2}{3} \times \frac{4}{5}$ f. $\frac{3}{4} \times \frac{1}{6}$

11. Now find the products of these, using multiplication only.

★ $\frac{7}{8} \times \frac{4}{5}$ ... $= \frac{7 \times 4}{8 \times 5} = \frac{28}{40}$

a. $\frac{6}{7} \times \frac{2}{3}$ b. $\frac{3}{4} \times \frac{7}{8}$

c. $\frac{7}{10} \times \frac{5}{9}$ d. $\frac{8}{9} \times \frac{7}{8}$

Multiplication of Fractions: Lowest Terms; Brackets

Reducing answers to lowest terms

Now that we know how to multiply a fraction by another fraction, we must be careful to **reduce the product to its lowest terms:**

For example,

$$\frac{7}{8} \times \frac{4}{5} = \frac{7 \times 4}{8 \times 5} = \frac{28}{40}$$

$\frac{28}{40}$ can be reduced to lowest terms:

$$\frac{28}{40} \begin{array}{c} \div 4 \\ \div 4 \end{array} = \frac{7}{10}$$

So, $\frac{7}{8} \times \frac{4}{5} = \frac{7}{10}$ (answer in its lowest terms)

Multiplication of 3 Fractions

Look at the multiplication of 3 whole numbers:

$$2 \times 3 \times 5$$
$$= (2 \times 3) \times 5 = 6 \times 5 = 30$$
$$= 2 \times (3 \times 5) = 2 \times 15 = 30$$
$$= (2 \times 5) \times 3 = 10 \times 3 = 30$$

The same thing can be done with fractions:

$$\frac{1}{2} \times \frac{1}{3} \times \frac{1}{5}$$

$$= \left(\frac{1}{2} \times \frac{1}{3}\right) \times \frac{1}{5} = \frac{1}{6} \times \frac{1}{5} = \frac{1}{30}$$

$$= \frac{1}{2} \times \left(\frac{1}{3} \times \frac{1}{5}\right) = \frac{1}{2} \times \frac{1}{15} = \frac{1}{30}$$

$$= \left(\frac{1}{2} \times \frac{1}{5}\right) \times \frac{1}{3} = \frac{1}{10} \times \frac{1}{3} = \frac{1}{30}$$

1. Solve these multiplications, writing each product in its lowest terms.

   a. $\frac{5}{6} \times \frac{2}{3}$ b. $\frac{7}{10} \times \frac{2}{3}$

   c. $\frac{4}{5} \times \frac{3}{4}$ d. $\frac{6}{7} \times \frac{3}{5}$

2. Solve these, using brackets to help you.

   ★ $\frac{1}{5} \times \frac{1}{3} \times \frac{1}{4} \cdots = \left(\frac{1}{5} \times \frac{1}{3}\right) \times \frac{1}{4}$

   $= \left(\frac{1 \times 1}{5 \times 3}\right) \times \frac{1}{4} = \frac{1}{15} \times \frac{1}{4} = \frac{1 \times 1}{15 \times 4}$

   $= \frac{1}{60}$

   a. $\frac{1}{2} \times \frac{1}{4} \times \frac{1}{5}$ b. $\frac{1}{5} \times \frac{1}{2} \times \frac{1}{3}$

   c. $\frac{1}{3} \times \frac{1}{3} \times \frac{1}{2}$ d. $\frac{1}{4} \times \frac{1}{5} \times \frac{1}{3}$

SID'S MAGIC FRACTION CORNER

Take any three fractional numbers, for example

$\frac{2}{5}, \frac{3}{4}$ and $\frac{2}{3}$

Multiply them: $\left(\frac{2}{5} \times \frac{3}{4}\right) \times \frac{2}{3}$

$$= \frac{6}{20} \times \frac{2}{3} = \frac{12}{60} = \frac{1}{5}$$

Now jumble them up and multiply them in a different order:

$\frac{2}{3} \times \frac{3}{4} \times \frac{2}{5}$ or $\frac{3}{4} \times \frac{2}{3} \times \frac{2}{5}$

What answers did you get? Yes, the same answer each time! Try out these sets:

   a. $\frac{1}{6}, \frac{3}{4}, \frac{4}{5}$ b. $\frac{2}{3}, \frac{5}{6}, \frac{1}{4}$

OXFORD
UNIVERSITY PRESS

Multiplication of Mixed Numbers: Cancelling

It's easy to solve multiplication sums containing mixed numbers, once we remember that we must change each mixed number into an improper fraction:

Examples: $1\frac{3}{4} \times 2$

$= \frac{7}{4} \times 2$

$= \frac{14}{4} = 3\frac{2}{4} = 3\frac{1}{2}$

(lowest terms)

$2\frac{1}{5} \times 1\frac{5}{6}$

$= \frac{11}{5} \times \frac{11}{6} = \frac{11 \times 11}{5 \times 6}$

$= \frac{121}{30} = 4\frac{1}{30}$

Sid has a useful short cut which he often uses when multiplying fractions.

For example, Sid wants to find the product of. $4\frac{2}{5} \times 3\frac{3}{4}$

He first changes his mixed numbers into improper fractions:

$4\frac{2}{5} \times 3\frac{3}{4} = \frac{22 \times 15}{5 \times 4}$

It's bothersome for Sid to multiply 22 by 15!

So he looks for a short cut.

He notices that the denominator of the first fraction and the numerator of the second fraction have common factors.

$$\frac{\overset{\div 2}{\cancel{22}} \times 15}{5 \times \underset{\div 2}{\cancel{4}}}$$

$$= \frac{11 \times \overset{\div 5}{\cancel{15}}}{\underset{\div 5}{\cancel{5}} \times 2} = \frac{11 \times 3}{1 \times 2} = \frac{33}{2} = 16\frac{1}{2}$$

▶ 1. Solve these multiplications making sure each product is in its lowest terms.

a. $2\frac{2}{5} \times 3$

b. $4\frac{1}{2} \times \frac{7}{8}$

c. $1\frac{5}{8} \times 2\frac{1}{4}$

d. $5 \times 4\frac{1}{8}$

e. $3\frac{1}{9} \times \frac{1}{3}$

f. $2\frac{1}{10} \times 1\frac{3}{8}$

g. $3\frac{3}{8} \times 6$

h. $2\frac{1}{4} \times \frac{1}{3}$

i. $3\frac{1}{4} \times 2\frac{7}{8}$

j. $\frac{1}{4} \times 2\frac{2}{3}$

k. $3\frac{3}{5} \times 1\frac{1}{2}$

l. $5\frac{1}{3} \times 1\frac{5}{6}$

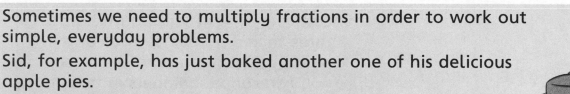

Sometimes we need to multiply fractions in order to work out simple, everyday problems.

Sid, for example, has just baked another one of his delicious apple pies.

Greedy as ever, he decides to keep $\frac{3}{4}$ of it for himself.

For lunch he eats $\frac{2}{3}$ of the portion he has kept for himself.

What fraction of the whole pie has he eaten?

He has eaten $\frac{2}{3} \times \frac{3}{4} = \frac{\overset{1}{\cancel{2}} \times \cancel{3}}{\cancel{3} \times \cancel{4}_2} = \frac{1}{2}$

Sid has eaten exactly $\frac{1}{2}$ of the pie.

1. Think carefully, then solve these word problems, writing complete statements.

   a. In a class of 44 pupils, $\frac{3}{4}$ are girls. How many girls are there altogether? How many boys? Answer in (i) numbers and (ii) fractions.

   b. Ayesha's grandmother buys $\frac{3}{4}$ m of lace for her handkerchief. She uses only $\frac{2}{3}$ of the lace. What length of lace has she used?

   c. If the geography textbook for Class 5 is $\frac{4}{5}$ cm thick, how high will a pile of 9 such textbooks be?

2. Now solve these, think carefully and make complete statements.

   a. On Purple Grass Farm in Superglobe, $\frac{2}{3}$ of the land is used for growing vegetables. Space-fingers are grown on $\frac{1}{4}$ of this portion. What fraction of the total farm area is devoted to space-fingers?

   b. The racetrack in Planet City Stadium is $1\frac{7}{8}$ km long. If Sprog Spacewalker manages to run around it $4\frac{1}{3}$ times before collapsing, how many km has he run?

Sid's Magic Fraction Page

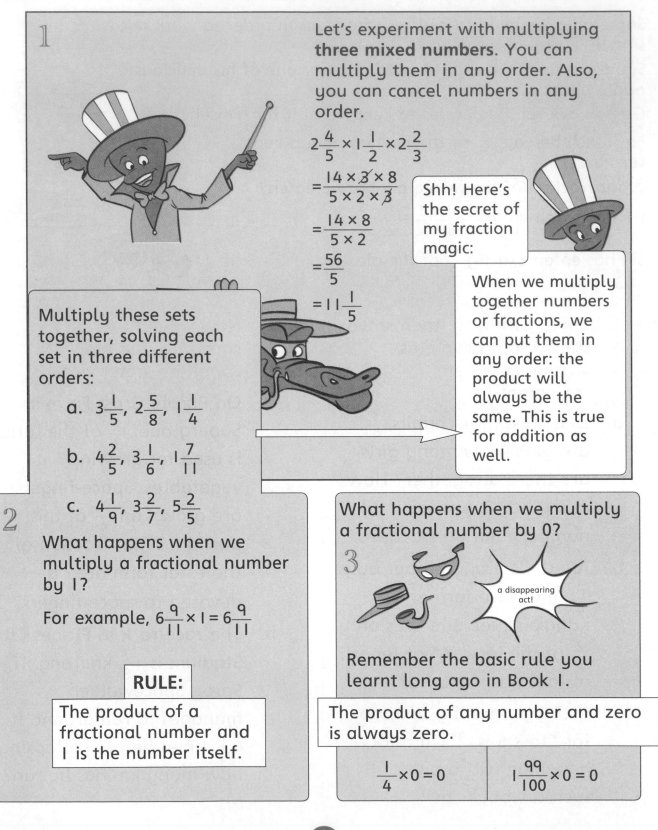

1

Let's experiment with multiplying **three mixed numbers**. You can multiply them in any order. Also, you can cancel numbers in any order.

$$2\frac{4}{5} \times 1\frac{1}{2} \times 2\frac{2}{3}$$

$$= \frac{14 \times 3 \times 8}{5 \times 2 \times 3}$$

$$= \frac{14 \times 8}{5 \times 2}$$

$$= \frac{56}{5}$$

$$= 11\frac{1}{5}$$

Shh! Here's the secret of my fraction magic:

When we multiply together numbers or fractions, we can put them in any order: the product will always be the same. This is true for addition as well.

Multiply these sets together, solving each set in three different orders:

a. $3\frac{1}{5}$, $2\frac{5}{8}$, $1\frac{1}{4}$

b. $4\frac{2}{5}$, $3\frac{1}{6}$, $1\frac{7}{11}$

c. $4\frac{1}{9}$, $3\frac{2}{7}$, $5\frac{2}{5}$

2

What happens when we multiply a fractional number by 1?

For example, $6\frac{9}{11} \times 1 = 6\frac{9}{11}$

RULE:

The product of a fractional number and 1 is the number itself.

3

What happens when we multiply a fractional number by 0?

a disappearing act!

Remember the basic rule you learnt long ago in Book 1.

The product of any number and zero is always zero.

$\frac{1}{4} \times 0 = 0$	$1\frac{99}{100} \times 0 = 0$

Sid is looking back through his old, school textbooks. He has found his old, battered copy of Book 1.

Sid is reviewing the basic rules of division.

When we want an answer to 21 ÷ 3, we ask ourselves, 'how many sets of three can be made from a set of 21', or, more simply, 'how many threes make 21?' This is far too easy for Sid and for you! If we remember this basic rule of division, we shall find division with fractions simple and fun to do.

1. Copy and complete this table, remembering your rules of division.

★ Division sum	Words we say	Quotient
72 ÷ 9	How many nines make 72?	8
2500 ÷ 50		
324 ÷ 4		
391 ÷ 17		

2. Write in numbers.

★ How many twelves make 144?

$$144 ÷ 12 = 12$$

a. How many 16s make 832?

b. How many 21s in 903?

c. How many 19s make 1083?

d. How many 35s in 595?

Basic Rules of Division for Fractions

Using words to help us, we can easily solve this division.

$$1 ÷ \frac{1}{4}$$

We ask ourselves: **how many quarters make one whole?**
The answer is easy: 4 quarters make 1 whole.

$$1 ÷ \frac{1}{4} = 4$$

Now let us try this: $2 ÷ \frac{1}{3}$

We ask ourselves: **how many thirds are needed to make two wholes?**
Again, the answer is easy: 6 thirds make 2 wholes.

$$2 ÷ \frac{1}{3} = 6$$

3. Now solve these, using words to help you.

a. $1 ÷ \frac{1}{3}$ b. $1 ÷ \frac{1}{8}$ c. $3 ÷ \frac{1}{3}$

d. $1 ÷ \frac{1}{5}$ e. $2 ÷ \frac{1}{4}$ f. $3 ÷ \frac{1}{5}$

4. Copy and complete this table, thinking very carefully.

★

Division sum	In words	Quotient
$2 \div \frac{1}{3}$	How many thirds make 2 wholes?	6
a. $3 \div \frac{1}{7}$		
b. $9 \div \frac{1}{10}$		
c. $12 \div \frac{1}{11}$		132
d. $14 \div \frac{1}{12}$		

Look at your completed table carefully. Have you noticed something interesting?

To find the quotient of each **division**, you have been using **multiplication**! For example, to solve this:

$$18 \div \frac{1}{14}$$

We ask ourselves:

How many fourteenths in 18?

We know that there are 14 fourteenths in one whole.

So, there are 18 × 14 (252) fourteenths in 18 wholes.

$$18 \div \frac{1}{14} = 252$$

When we divide with fractions, we use multiplication to help us.

5. Write division sums to match these diagrams.

★ ⊕⊕⊕ $3 \div \frac{1}{4}$
    = 12 quarters

a.

b.

c.

d.

6. Now complete these with the help of diagrams.

a. $6 \div \frac{1}{9}$ b. $30 \div \frac{1}{20}$

c. $13 \div \frac{1}{14}$ d. $28 \div \frac{1}{7}$

e. $18 \div \frac{1}{15}$ f. $7 \div \frac{1}{12}$

g. $32 \div \frac{1}{17}$ h. $17 \div \frac{1}{19}$

i. $14 \div \frac{1}{13}$ j. $23 \div \frac{1}{4}$

k. $11 \div \frac{1}{10}$ l. $43 \div \frac{1}{11}$

7. Write the reciprocals of the following.

★ $\frac{5}{9}$ ... $\frac{9}{5}$

a. $\frac{2}{3}$ b. $\frac{7}{8}$ c. $\frac{1}{12}$

8. Find the reciprocals of these.

★ $2\frac{1}{2} = \frac{5}{2}$ ... reciprocal = $\frac{2}{5}$

a. $1\frac{1}{2}$ b. $2\frac{2}{3}$ c. $1\frac{5}{8}$

Look at this:

$$2 \times \frac{1}{2}$$

When we use a whole number in a calculation involving fractions, we write our whole number in fractional form, thus:

$$2 \times \frac{1}{2} = \frac{2}{①} \times \frac{1}{2} = \frac{2 \times 1}{① \times 2} = \frac{2}{2} = 1$$

The denominator 1 tells us that the number is a whole number.

RULE When two numbers multiply to give 1, they are said to be the reciprocals of each other.

1. Write these whole numbers as fractions.

★ $3 = \frac{3}{1}$

a. 4   b. 12   c. 100

2. Write these numbers as fractions and then write the reciprocal of each.

★ $15 \dots \frac{15}{1}$ reciprocal $= \frac{1}{15}$

a. 10   b. 21   c. 2397

3. Rewrite the numbers as fractions, and solve.

★ $9 \div 3 \dots = \frac{9}{1} \div \frac{3}{1} = \frac{9}{1} \times \frac{1}{3}$

$= \frac{9 \times 1}{1 \times 3} = \frac{9}{3} = \frac{3}{1} = 3$

a. $12 \div 2$ b. $36 \div 12$ c. $100 \div 25$

Remember: $1 \div \frac{1}{4} = 4$

is the same as $\frac{1}{1} \times \frac{4}{1} = \frac{1 \times 4}{1 \times 1} = \frac{4}{1} = 4$

And $2 \div \frac{1}{3} = 6 = \frac{2}{1} \times \frac{3}{1} = \frac{2 \times 3}{1 \times 1} = \frac{6}{1} = 6$

IMPORTANT RULE!
Division by a fraction is the same as multiplication by its reciprocal.

4. Now solve these.

★ $8 \div \frac{1}{5} \dots = \frac{8}{1} \times \frac{5}{1} = \frac{8 \times 5}{1 \times 1}$

$= \frac{40}{1} = 40$

a. $12 \div \frac{1}{3}$ b. $100 \div \frac{1}{10}$

c. $15 \div \frac{1}{5}$ d. $96 \div \frac{1}{2}$

5. Use the 'division by a fraction' rule to solve these.

★ $5 \div \frac{2}{5} \dots = \frac{5}{1} \div \frac{2}{5} = \frac{5}{1} \times \frac{5}{2}$

$= \frac{5 \times 5}{1 \times 2} = \frac{25}{2} = 12\frac{1}{2}$

a. $3 \div \frac{3}{4}$ b. $24 \div \frac{4}{5}$

OXFORD
UNIVERSITY PRESS

Reciprocals: Dividing Fractions by Whole Numbers

Let's now apply our rule to this division. Here, the divisor is a whole number:

Example: $\dfrac{1}{4} \div 2$

$$\dfrac{1}{4} \div 2 = \dfrac{1}{4} \times \dfrac{1}{2} = \dfrac{1}{8}$$

Look at the examples:

$$12 \div 4\dfrac{1}{2} = \dfrac{\overset{4}{\cancel{12}}}{1} \times \dfrac{2}{\underset{3}{\cancel{9}}} = \dfrac{8}{3} = 2\dfrac{2}{3}$$

$$6\dfrac{3}{7} \div 4\dfrac{1}{2} = \dfrac{\overset{5}{\cancel{45}}}{7} \times \dfrac{2}{\underset{1}{\cancel{9}}} = \dfrac{10}{7} = 1\dfrac{3}{7}$$

6. Now solve these.

a. $8\dfrac{3}{5} \div 6$ b. $3\dfrac{1}{8} \div 1\dfrac{3}{4}$

c. $\dfrac{2}{9} \div 4$ d. $\dfrac{3}{5} \div 4$

Dividing a Fractional Number by a Fractional Number

Look at this sum: $\dfrac{1}{2} \div \dfrac{1}{4}$

Using our 'division by a fraction' rule, we can easily find the answer:

$$\dfrac{1}{2} \div \dfrac{1}{4} = \dfrac{1}{2} \times \dfrac{4}{1} = \dfrac{1 \times \overset{2}{\cancel{4}}}{\underset{1}{\cancel{2}} \times 1} = \dfrac{2}{1} = 2$$

We use exactly the same method to solve a sum like this:

$$\dfrac{3}{4} \div \dfrac{5}{8}$$

This sum asks us to find how many five-eighths (of a whole) make three quarters (of a whole).

We solve it like this:

$$\dfrac{3}{4} \div \dfrac{5}{8} = \dfrac{3}{4} \times \dfrac{8}{5} = \dfrac{3 \times \overset{2}{\cancel{8}}}{\underset{1}{\cancel{4}} \times 5} = \dfrac{6}{5} = 1\dfrac{1}{5}$$

7. Solve these sums, using the 'division by a fraction' rule.

★ $\dfrac{1}{3} \div \dfrac{1}{4} = \dfrac{1 \times 4}{3 \times 1} = \dfrac{4}{3} = 1\dfrac{1}{3}$

a. $\dfrac{1}{2} \div \dfrac{1}{3}$ b. $\dfrac{1}{4} \div \dfrac{1}{2}$ c. $\dfrac{1}{4} \div \dfrac{1}{3}$

8. Now, work out the following.

★ $\dfrac{3}{4} \div \dfrac{2}{3} = \dfrac{3}{4} \times \dfrac{3}{2} = \dfrac{3 \times 3}{4 \times 2} = \dfrac{9}{8} = 1\dfrac{1}{8}$

a. $\dfrac{1}{2} \div \dfrac{3}{5}$ b. $\dfrac{1}{4} \div \dfrac{2}{5}$

9. Copy and fill in the blanks.

a. Dividing by $\dfrac{1}{2}$ is the same as multiplying by _____ .

b. Dividing by $\dfrac{4}{7}$ is the same as _____ by $\dfrac{7}{4}$.

OXFORD
UNIVERSITY PRESS

We can easily solve division sums involving mixed numbers: we simply turn our mixed numbers into improper fractions and apply our 'division by a fraction' rule:

Example A: $9\frac{1}{2} \div 3 = \frac{19}{2} \div \frac{3}{1}$

$$= \frac{19}{2} \times \frac{1}{3} = \frac{19 \times 1}{2 \times 3}$$

$$= \frac{19}{6} = 3\frac{1}{6}$$

Example B: $4\frac{3}{4} \div 2\frac{2}{5}$

$$= \frac{19}{4} \div \frac{12}{5}$$

$$= \frac{19}{4} \times \frac{5}{12} = \frac{19 \times 5}{4 \times 12}$$

$$= \frac{95}{48} = 1\frac{47}{48}$$

Sometimes, we may be able to cancel:

Example C: $2\frac{2}{3} \div 1\frac{1}{6}$

$$= \frac{8}{3} \div \frac{7}{6} = \frac{8}{3} \times \frac{6}{7}$$

$$= \frac{8 \times \overset{2}{\cancel{6}}}{\underset{1}{\cancel{3}} \times 7} = \frac{16}{7} = 2\frac{2}{7}$$

 1. Now, solve these divisions.

a. $10\frac{1}{2} \div 5$ b. $8\frac{3}{5} \div 6$

c. $5\frac{7}{9} \div 2\frac{1}{3}$ d. $18 \div 3\frac{1}{3}$

e. $16 \div 4\frac{3}{4}$ f. $3\frac{5}{6} \div 1\frac{1}{6}$

g. $4\frac{9}{10} \div 2\frac{1}{2}$ h. $12 \div 4\frac{1}{4}$

2. Now, solve these.

a. $8\frac{1}{4} \div 3\frac{5}{8}$ b. $5\frac{2}{5} \div 2\frac{4}{5}$

3. True or false? Think carefully, then write T or F.

a. The reciprocal of $\frac{1}{12}$ is 12.

b. $\frac{2}{3} \div \frac{1}{2}$ means 'how many halves make two-thirds'.

c. The reciprocal of $2\frac{2}{3}$ is $2\frac{3}{2}$.

d. The product of any two fractional numbers is always less than either of the two numbers.

e. The product of a fractional number and its reciprocal is always zero.

f. Each fractional number has only one reciprocal.

g. The reciprocal of $\frac{1}{1000}$ is 1000.

h. $\frac{3}{4} \div \frac{1}{4}$ is the same as $\frac{3}{4}$ of $\frac{4}{1}$.

Oh Dear! Sweet friend! How happy I am to see you!

OXFORD
UNIVERSITY PRESS

More Fraction Magic

Turn back to page 74. There we discovered some magic facts about multiplying with fractions.

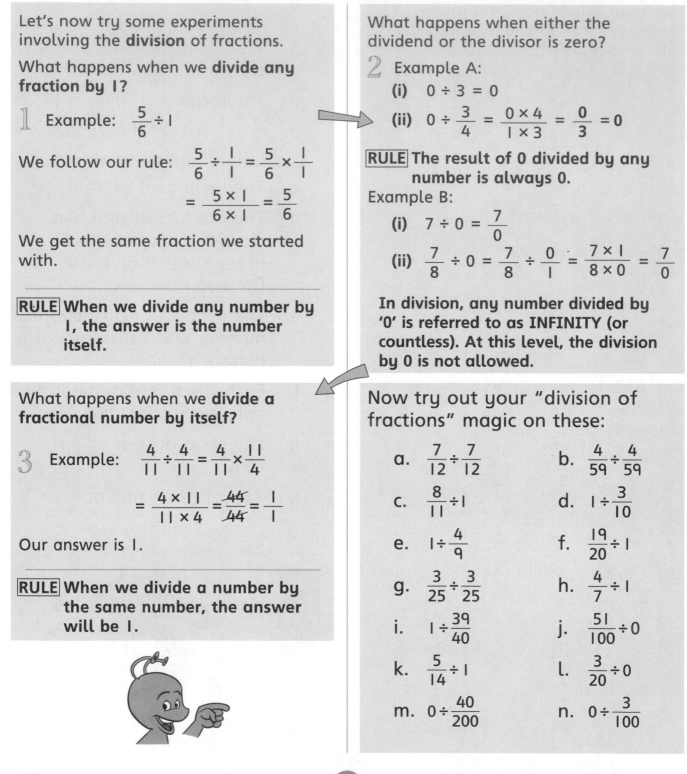

Let's now try some experiments involving the **division** of fractions.

What happens when we **divide any fraction by 1?**

1 Example: $\frac{5}{6} \div 1$

We follow our rule: $\frac{5}{6} \div \frac{1}{1} = \frac{5}{6} \times \frac{1}{1}$

$$= \frac{5 \times 1}{6 \times 1} = \frac{5}{6}$$

We get the same fraction we started with.

RULE When we divide any number by 1, the answer is the number itself.

What happens when we **divide a fractional number by itself?**

3 Example: $\frac{4}{11} \div \frac{4}{11} = \frac{4}{11} \times \frac{11}{4}$

$$= \frac{4 \times 11}{11 \times 4} = \frac{\cancel{44}}{\cancel{44}} = \frac{1}{1}$$

Our answer is 1.

RULE When we divide a number by the same number, the answer will be 1.

What happens when either the dividend or the divisor is zero?

2 Example A:

(i) $0 \div 3 = 0$

(ii) $0 \div \frac{3}{4} = \frac{0 \times 4}{1 \times 3} = \frac{0}{3} = 0$

RULE The result of 0 divided by any number is always 0.

Example B:

(i) $7 \div 0 = \frac{7}{0}$

(ii) $\frac{7}{8} \div 0 = \frac{7}{8} \div \frac{0}{1} = \frac{7 \times 1}{8 \times 0} = \frac{7}{0}$

In division, any number divided by '0' is referred to as INFINITY (or countless). At this level, the division by 0 is not allowed.

Now try out your "division of fractions" magic on these:

a. $\frac{7}{12} \div \frac{7}{12}$ b. $\frac{4}{59} \div \frac{4}{59}$

c. $\frac{8}{11} \div 1$ d. $1 \div \frac{3}{10}$

e. $1 \div \frac{4}{9}$ f. $\frac{19}{20} \div 1$

g. $\frac{3}{25} \div \frac{3}{25}$ h. $\frac{4}{7} \div 1$

i. $1 \div \frac{39}{40}$ j. $\frac{51}{100} \div 0$

k. $\frac{5}{14} \div 1$ l. $\frac{3}{20} \div 0$

m. $0 \div \frac{40}{200}$ n. $0 \div \frac{3}{100}$

Division with Fractions: Word Problems

Sid has been baking again. This time, he has baked a rich, dark chocolate cake with cherries on top.

He eats $\frac{1}{2}$ the cake. The other $\frac{1}{2}$ he shares among Sara, Sue, Selvi and Sprog. Each gets $\frac{1}{4}$ of $\frac{1}{2}$ cake.

How much of the whole cake will each of them receive?

We use our 'division with fractions' rule to find out:

4 family members share $\frac{1}{2}$ of the cake.

So each family member gets

$$\frac{1}{2} \div 4 = \frac{1}{2} \div \frac{4}{1}$$

$$= \frac{1}{2} \times \frac{1}{4} = \frac{1 \times 1}{2 \times 4} = \frac{1}{8}$$

Each family member (other than Sid) gets $\frac{1}{8}$ of the cake.

$$\frac{1}{2} \div 4 = \frac{1}{4} \text{ of } \frac{1}{2} = \frac{1}{8}$$

1. Now solve these problems, making complete statements.

a. A pile of maths textbooks on a table is exactly $14\frac{2}{5}$ cm high. If each book is $1\frac{1}{5}$ cm thick, how many books make up the pile?

b. Maham has 36 chocolates. She gives $\frac{4}{9}$ of them to her best friend, Laila, then shares the rest between herself and 4 other friends. How many chocolates does Maham get?

c. A piece of ribbon is $5\frac{3}{5}$ m long. If it is cut into 14 equal pieces, how long will each piece be? Write your answer (i) in fractions (ii) in m and cm.

d. In the Shooting Star Restaurant, Outer Space, a pancake takes just $\frac{1}{5}$ of a minute to cook. How many pancakes can be cooked in the space of $1\frac{1}{2}$ hours?

OXFORD
UNIVERSITY PRESS

Simplification with Fractions

Look at this:

$$1\frac{1}{4} \div \frac{1}{2} \times 3$$

$$= \left(\frac{5}{4} \times \frac{2}{1}\right) \times 3$$

$$= \frac{5}{2} \times 3$$

$$= \frac{15}{2}$$

$$= 7\frac{1}{2}$$

Divide
Multiply
Add
Subtract

We have used the DMAS rule here.

Look at this:

$$\left\{4\frac{1}{2} + \left(5\frac{1}{3} \div 2\right)\right\} - 1\frac{1}{2}$$

$$= \left\{4\frac{1}{2} + \left(\frac{16}{3} \times \frac{1}{2}\right)\right\} - 1\frac{1}{2}$$

$$= \left\{4\frac{1}{2} + \frac{8}{3}\right\} - 1\frac{1}{2}$$

$$= \left\{\frac{9}{2} + \frac{8}{3}\right\} - 1\frac{1}{2}$$

$$= \left\{\frac{27+16}{6}\right\} - 1\frac{1}{2}$$

$$= \frac{43}{6} - \frac{3}{2}$$

$$= \frac{43-9}{6} = \frac{\overset{17}{\cancel{34}}}{\underset{3}{\cancel{6}}}$$

$$= \frac{17}{3} = 5\frac{2}{3}$$

1. Using the DMAS rule to help you, solve these.

   a. $3\frac{1}{2} + 5\frac{5}{6} - 1\frac{1}{4}$

   b. $4\frac{1}{8} \div 2 - 1\frac{7}{8}$

   c. $5\frac{3}{5} \times 1\frac{1}{4} + 10\frac{3}{4}$

   D for Do
   M for Maths
   A for After
   S for Supper

   d. $18 - 6\frac{2}{3} \div 4$

   e. $5 \div 2\frac{7}{8} \times 10\frac{2}{5}$

   f. $4\frac{9}{10} \times 1\frac{2}{7} + 10\frac{2}{5}$

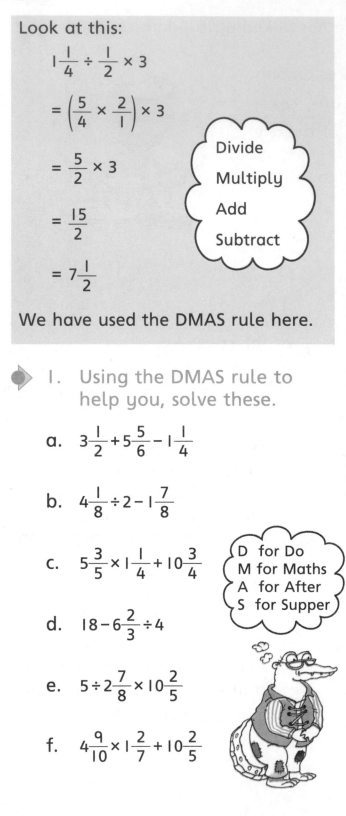

2. Working very carefully, solve these.

   a. $\left(1\frac{1}{4} + 2\frac{2}{3}\right) \times \left(3\frac{1}{3} + 2\frac{1}{2}\right)$

   b. $4\frac{1}{2} + \left\{\left(3\frac{3}{5} - 1\frac{3}{4}\right) \times 5\right\}$

   c. $\left\{\left(18 \div 6\frac{2}{3}\right) + 14\frac{3}{4}\right\} - 2\frac{1}{2}$

   d. $20 + \left[5 \times \left\{9 - \left(1\frac{2}{3} \times \frac{1}{5}\right)\right\}\right]$

   e. $24 + \left[3 \times \left\{10\frac{1}{2} - \left(\frac{5}{6} \div \frac{1}{3}\right)\right\}\right]$

   f. $\left[12\frac{1}{2} + \left\{3\frac{3}{4} \times \left(\frac{1}{2} + \frac{2}{5}\right)\right\}\right] - 2\frac{1}{2}$

   g. $\left\{4\frac{1}{2} + \left(5\frac{1}{3} \times 3\right)\right\} - 2\frac{2}{3}$

REVIEW

Fractions

1. Copy and complete the table.

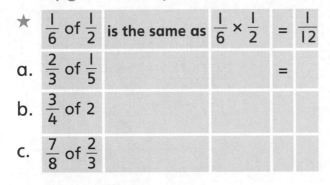

★ $\frac{1}{6}$ of $\frac{1}{2}$	is the same as	$\frac{1}{6} \times \frac{1}{2}$	=	$\frac{1}{12}$
a. $\frac{2}{3}$ of $\frac{1}{5}$			=	
b. $\frac{3}{4}$ of 2				
c. $\frac{7}{8}$ of $\frac{2}{3}$				

2. Solve these, making sure each answer is in its lowest terms.

   a. $\frac{5}{8} \times \frac{3}{4} \times 1$ b. $\frac{2}{3} \times \frac{5}{6} \times 0$

   c. $1\frac{5}{6} \times \frac{7}{11}$ d. $3\frac{1}{8} \times \frac{2}{5}$

3. Write the reciprocals of the following.

   a. $21\frac{1}{5}$ b. $10\frac{4}{5}$

   c. $2\frac{1}{4}$ d. $\frac{1}{999}$

   e. 100   f. $15\frac{1}{3}$

4. Solve these.

   a. $18 \div \frac{3}{4}$ b. $\frac{1}{4} \div \frac{2}{3}$

   c. $\frac{1}{8} \div 3$ d. $1 \div \frac{15}{16}$

5. Solve these, thinking carefully about which operation you need to use. Make complete statements.

   a. Babar starts the day with 15 kg of potatoes for sale in his shop. He sells $4\frac{2}{5}$ kg before 10 a.m. and $6\frac{1}{10}$ kg between 10 a.m. and noon. What weight is left over for the afternoon? Give your answer (i) in fractions; (ii) in kg and g.

   b. Selvi Spacewalker took $\frac{3}{4}$ hours to draw a picture of Venus. Sid took only $\frac{4}{5}$ of the same period of time to draw a picture of Saturn. How long did Sid take to complete his picture? Give your answer (i) in minutes; (ii) as a fraction of an hour.

6. Solve these, working very carefully.

   a. $\left(6\frac{1}{3} + 2\frac{4}{9}\right) - \left(1 \times \frac{7}{8}\right)$

   b. $\left\{3 \times \left(1\frac{1}{4} \div \frac{5}{8}\right)\right\} - 2\frac{5}{6}$

   c. $3\frac{1}{2} + \left[5 \times \left\{16 - \left(3\frac{1}{4} - 2\frac{2}{5}\right)\right\}\right]$

OXFORD
UNIVERSITY PRESS

Help Sid and Sara review the links between common fractions and decimal fractions by doing these puzzles:

Colour squares to show the fraction, then write in decimal form:

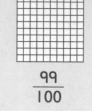

1

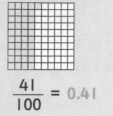

$\frac{41}{100} = 0.41$

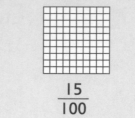

$\frac{7}{10}$

$\frac{15}{100}$

$\frac{5}{100}$

$\frac{99}{100}$

2

Complete the table:

$\frac{1}{100}$	0.01
$\frac{2}{10}$	
	0.47
$\frac{3}{1000}$	
	0.8
$\frac{19}{1000}$	
$\frac{245}{1000}$	
	0.69
$\frac{7}{10}$	
	0.732
$\frac{14}{100}$	

Now do the crossword: 3

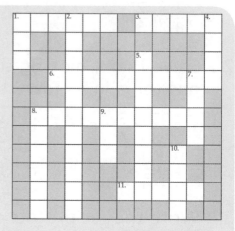

Clues Across:

1. In the number 65.2, the '2' is in the _____ column.
3. When we divide a number by 10, that number jumps one column to the _____ (Think carefully!)
6. 0.17 is the same as seventeen _____
8. The decimal point separates a whole number from a _____ number.
11. Six _____ zero one is the same as $6\frac{1}{100}$.

Clues Down:

1. 0.2 is the same as _____ tenths.
2. 0.019 is the same as nineteen _____
4. In the number 460.19, the '6' is in the _____ column.
5. When we write $\frac{2}{1000}$ as a decimal, we say 'zero point _____ _____ two.

7. When we see 0.5, we know it equals one _____ in common fraction form.
8. For a fraction to have an equivalent decimal fraction its denominator must be a _____ of 10, 100 or 1000.
9. 0.010 is the same as _____ thousandths.
10. In the number 83.095, the digit in the hundredths column is _____

1. Write these common fractions as decimals by changing them into equivalent fractions with denominator 10, when necessary.

   ★ $2\frac{1}{2} = 2\frac{5}{10} = 2.5$

   ★ $1\frac{8}{10} = 1.8$

   ★ $5\frac{3}{5} = 5\frac{6}{10} = 5.6$

   a. $3\frac{1}{2}$ b. $\frac{1}{10}$ c. $2\frac{7}{10}$

   d. $100\frac{1}{2}$ e. $10\frac{3}{5}$ f. $3\frac{4}{5}$

2. Change into common fractions.

   ★ $12.95 = 12\frac{95}{100} = 12\frac{19}{20}$

   a. 10.01   b. 18.05   c. 35.75

   d. 25.25   e. 33.04   f. 100.2

3. Write these lengths in cm.

   ★ 18 cm 5 mm = 18.5 cm

   a. 6 cm 5 mm   b. 15 cm 9 mm

   c. 10 cm 1 mm   d. 8 cm 7 mm

4. Copy and fill in the missing symbols (+, −, × or ÷).

   ★ 4 ____ 10 = 0.4 ... 4 ÷ 10 = 0.4

   a. 0.06 ____ 10 = 0.6

   b. 5.91 ____ 10 = 0.591

   c. 9.1 ____ 2.1 = 7

   d. 2.02 ____ 1.01 = 3.03

5. Write numbers to match the statements.

   ★ 8 in the hundredths place, 1 in the ones place, 3 in the tenths place. ... 1.38

   a. 9 in the ones place , 4 in the tens place, 6 in the hundredths place, 0 in the tenths place.

   b. 0 in the hundredths place, 5 in the thousandths place, 0 in the tenths place, 9 in the ones place.

6. Write as decimals.

   ★ $1\frac{3}{1000} = 1.003$

   a. $2\frac{5}{1000}$ b. $8\frac{9}{100}$ c. $200\frac{9}{10}$

   d. $4\frac{21}{1000}$ e. $\frac{117}{1000}$ f. $15\frac{5}{100}$

7. Write the place of the coloured digit.

   ★ 93.061 ... 1 thousandth

   a. 14.032   b. 492.032

   c. 25.174   d. 645.53

8. Write these as decimals by first changing them into equivalent fractions with denominators of 10, 100 or 1000.

   ★ $14\frac{3}{250} = 14\frac{3}{250}^{\times 4}_{\times 4} = 14\frac{12}{1000}$

   a. $3\frac{4}{25}$ b. $8\frac{7}{200}$ c. $14\frac{65}{500}$

OXFORD
UNIVERSITY PRESS

Comparing Decimals: Review Page

1. Copy in your notebook, then fill in <, >, or =.

   ★ 0.3 > 0.03

   a. $\frac{8}{100}$ ⬛ $\frac{8}{10}$

   b. $\frac{10}{1000}$ ⬛ $\frac{1}{100}$

   c. 0.004 ⬛ 0.040

   d. 1.75 ⬛ $1\frac{75}{100}$

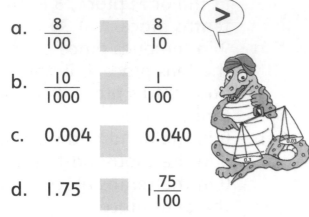

2. Look carefully at these sets, then rewrite them in ascending order.

   ★ 0.93, 0.039, 0.932, 0.009

   ... 0.009, 0.039, 0.93, 0.932

   a. $\frac{17}{100}, \frac{17}{1000}, \frac{173}{1000}, \frac{13}{100}$

   b. 18.413, 18.143, 18.341, 18.431

   c. 0.012, 0.12, 0.002, 0.001

   d. $\frac{3}{50}, \frac{5}{100}, \frac{1}{25}, \frac{90}{1000}$

3. Now place the numbers in these sets in descending order.

   ★ $\frac{18}{100}, \frac{2}{10}, \frac{18}{1000}, \frac{81}{1000}$

   ... $\frac{2}{10}, \frac{18}{100}, \frac{81}{1000}, \frac{18}{1000}$

   a. 5.063, 5.6, 5.003, 5.36

   b. 11.064, 11.604, 11.406, 11.1

   c. $\frac{8}{100}, \frac{6}{50}, \frac{4}{25}, \frac{1}{20}$

4. Tick (✓) the largest decimal number in each set.

   a. 18.95, 18.90, 18.05

   b. 600.60, 600.65, 606.05

5. Think carefully, then tick (✓) the shortest length in each set.

   a. $4\frac{2}{5}$ cm, 4.5 cm, 0.4 m

   b. $1\frac{1}{1000}$ cm, 100 cm, 1002 m

Addition and Subtraction with Decimals: Review

Remember how we set out decimal fractions in a place-value table:

	H	T	O	.	t	h	th
42.3 =		4	2	.	3		
118.61 =	1	1	8	.	6	1	
4.993 =			4	.	9	9	3

The first number, 42.3, has only 1 digit, 3, to the right of the decimal point. It has only **1 decimal place (dp)**. We can also write it as $42\frac{3}{10}$. The second number, 118.61, has 2 digits, to the right of the decimal point. It has **2 decimal places**. We can also write it as $118\frac{61}{100}$. The last number, 4.993, has 3 digits, to the right of the decimal point. It therefore has **3 decimal places**. We can also write it as $4\frac{993}{1000}$.

When we work with decimals, it is very important to write our sums neatly, with the decimal point and the columns properly aligned. Each number above has a different number of decimal places. Such number places are called **unlike decimals**.

We can easily transform them into **like decimals** with three decimal places each:

H	T	O	.	t	h	th
	4	2	.	3	0	0
1	1	8	.	6	1	0
		4	.	9	9	3

All three numbers are now like decimals!

Look at this:

```
    9.803          Rs 56.19
 + 15.434        − Rs 23.48
   25.237          Rs 32.71
```

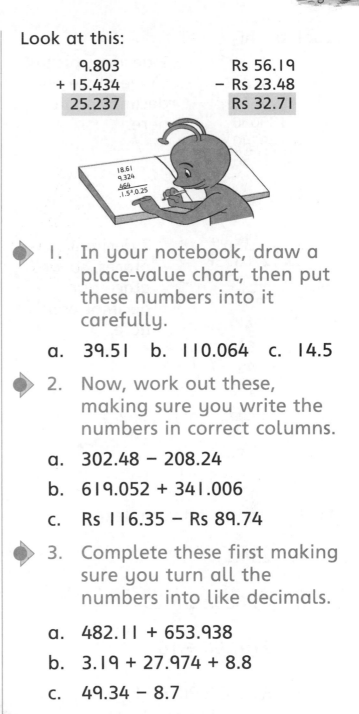

1. In your notebook, draw a place-value chart, then put these numbers into it carefully.

   a. 39.51   b. 110.064   c. 14.5

2. Now, work out these, making sure you write the numbers in correct columns.

   a. 302.48 − 208.24

   b. 619.052 + 341.006

   c. Rs 116.35 − Rs 89.74

3. Complete these first making sure you turn all the numbers into like decimals.

   a. 482.11 + 653.938

   b. 3.19 + 27.974 + 8.8

   c. 49.34 − 8.7

   d. 732.11 − 28.932

OXFORD
UNIVERSITY PRESS

Multiplication and Division with Decimals

Look at this

```
      174.62      2 decimal places,
    ×    28       so we place our
    ─────────     decimal point
     139696       here.
     349240
    ─────────
    4889.36
```

```
        112.64    2 decimal
    24)2703.36    places, so we
       24         place our
      ────        decimal point
        30        here.
        24
       ────
        63
        48
       ────
       153
       144
       ────
        96
        96
       ────
        --
```

1. Copy and complete:

a. 234.11 × 18

b. Rs 625.50 × 25

c. 2707.68 ÷ 16

d. Rs 1929.90 × 11

e. 2213.40 ÷ 68

f. 861.421 ÷ 11

2. Find the value of the following.

a. 2.4 × 3   b. 7.905 × 3

c. 10.5 × 2   d. 4.672 × 5

e. 5.6 × 7   f. 3.187 × 9

g. 19.56 × 8   h. 0.998 × 15

i. 21.33 × 9   j. 1.767 × 21

k. 212.35 × 5   l. 2.438 × 18

m. 8.96 × 12   n. 8.752 × 26

3. Now find the value of these.

a. 13.6 ÷ 4   b. 14.56 ÷ 7

c. 14.5 ÷ 5   d. 21.95 ÷ 5

e. 27.2 ÷ 8   f. 72.84 ÷ 4

g. 5.2 ÷ 4   h. 42.07 ÷ 7

i. 2.79 ÷ 3   j. 1.26 ÷ 6

k. 113.88 ÷12   l. 3.75 ÷ 5

m. 83.93 ÷ 11   n. 76.86 ÷ 9

o. 12.08 ÷ 2   p. 149.85 ÷ 15

Multiplying Decimal Numbers by 10, 100, and 1000

We know that when we multiply a whole number by 10, that number jumps one column on the left. The decimal point jumps one column to the right.

$$37 \times 10 = 370$$

H	T	O	.	t
	3	7	.	0

$\times\ 10\ =$

H	T	O	.	t
3	7	0	.	0

What happens when we multiply a number with a decimal point by 10?

$$3.7 \times 10 = ?$$

$$3.7 \times 10 = 3\frac{7}{10} \times 10 = \frac{37}{\cancel{10}} \times \frac{\cancel{10}}{1} = 37$$

$$3.7 \times 10 = 37$$

RULE

When we multiply a number with a decimal point by 10, we apply the same rule as for whole numbers: Move one column to the LEFT!

1. Multiply the following numbers by 10.

   a. 59.6   b. 129.8

   c. 364.8   d. 730.1

   e. 469.78   f. 341.0

   g. 3463.7   h. 734.9

Let us see what happens when we multiply a decimal number:

$$3.7 \times 100 = 3\frac{7}{10} \times 100$$

$$= \frac{37}{\cancel{10}_1} \times \frac{\cancel{100}^{10}}{1} = \frac{370}{1}$$

Answer: **3.7 × 100 = 370**

Our number has now jumped 2 columns to the left:

H	T	O	.	t	h
	3	.	7	0	

$\times\ 100\ =$

H	T	O	.	t	h
3	7	0	.	0	0

We can guess what will happen when we multiply by 1000:

$$3.7 \times 1000 = \frac{37}{\cancel{10}_1} \times \cancel{1000}^{100} = 3700$$

Our number has now jumped 3 columns to the left:

H	T	O	.	t	h	th
	3	.	7	0	0	

$\times 1000 =$

T	H	T	O	.	t	h	th
3	7	0	0	.	0	0	0

2. Multiply the numbers after changing decimal numbers into common fractions.

   a. 5.3   × 100
   b. 4.96   × 100
   c. 1.9   × 1000
   d. 395.678   × 1000
   e. 0.08   × 1000
   f. 70.01   × 100
   g. 35.635   × 1000
   h. 0.002   × 10
   i. 29.3   × 10

OXFORD
UNIVERSITY PRESS

Dividing a Number with a Decimal Point by 10 and its Multiples

In Book 4, number 48,000 had a Dreadful Division Disaster.

When divided by 10, the number 48,000 moved one column to the right and lost one of its zeros, becoming 4800.

When divided by 100, it moved two columns to the right, losing two of its zeros to become 480.

When divided by 1000, it moved three columns to the right, losing three zeros to become 48!

We apply the same rule when we divide a number with a decimal point by 10 or its multiples:

$$8.3 \div 10 = 0.83$$

If divided by **10**, our number jumps **one column** to the right.

$$8.3 \div 100 = 0.083$$

If divided by **100**, our number jumps **two columns** to the right.

$$8.3 \div 1000 = 0.0083 \text{ (three zeros)}$$

If divided by **1000**, our number jumps **three columns** to the right.

| RULE | Count the zeros in your divisor, then shift your dividend the same number of columns to the right! |

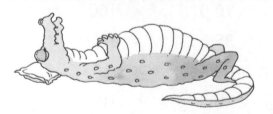

1. Copy and complete the divisions.

    a. $3.18 \div 10$ b. $6.51 \div 100$

    c. $6.24 \div 10$ d. $6.94 \div 100$

    e. $8.3 \div 100$ f. $4.83 \div 100$

    g. $4.1 \div 1000$ h. $4.5 \div 1000$

2. Think carefully, then fill in the blanks.

    ★ $5.5 \div \underline{\hspace{1cm}} = 0.55$

    ... $5.5 \div 10 = 0.55$ (dividend has moved 1 column to the right)

    a. $3.6 \div \underline{\hspace{1cm}} = 0.36$

    b. $4.8 \div \underline{\hspace{1cm}} = 0.048$

    c. $1.92 \div \underline{\hspace{1cm}} = 0.192$

    d. $8.74 \div \underline{\hspace{1cm}} = 0.0874$

3. Which number should replace the question mark?

1000	43.5	0.0435
100	13.2	?
10	4.7	0.47

OXFORD
UNIVERSITY PRESS

Multiplying by a Decimal (tenths only)

Sid wants to work out the area of this piece of graph paper:

37 mm

29 mm

1 cm²

Each little square has an area of 1mm². Sid's answer will be:

$$37 \text{ mm} \times 29 \text{ mm} = 1073 \text{ mm}^2$$
$$\text{Area} = 1073 \text{ mm}^2$$

But Sid wants to use **cm**, instead. He knows that 37 mm = 3.7 cm and that 29 mm = 2.9 cm

He therefore needs to work like this
$$3.7 \times 2.9 \text{ cm}^2$$

He can do so by changing the numbers with decimals into common fractions:

3.7 cm × 2.9 cm

$$= 3\frac{7}{10} \text{ cm} \times 2\frac{9}{10} \text{ cm}$$

$$= \frac{37}{10} \text{ cm} \times \frac{29}{10} \text{ cm} = \frac{1073}{100} \text{ cm}^2$$

$$= 10\frac{73}{100} \text{ cm}^2 = 10.73 \text{ cm}^2$$

Area = 10.73 cm²

Look at Sid's answers:

(1)   Area = 1073 mm²

(2)   Area = 10.73 cm²

If Sid divides answer (1) by 100,

he gets answer (2): $\frac{1073}{100} = 10.73$

∴ 1 cm² = 100 mm²

1. Help Sid work out the area of these pieces of graph paper, (i) in mm² and (ii) in cm².

★

32 mm

22 mm

(i)   32 mm × 22 mm = 704 mm²

Area = 704 mm²

(ii)   3.2 cm × 2.2 cm

$$= \frac{32}{10} \times \frac{22}{10} \text{ cm}^2 = \frac{704}{100} = 7\frac{4}{100}$$

Area = 7.04 cm²

a.

43 mm

27 mm

b.

48 mm

34 mm

2. Work out these areas, (i) in mm² and (ii) in cm².

a. 16 mm × 42 mm

b. 57 mm × 28 mm

c. 84 mm × 65 mm

Remember: 1 cm² = 100 mm²

OXFORD
UNIVERSITY PRESS

Multiplying by a Decimal (tenths only)

Look at this 1 cm square (enlarged):

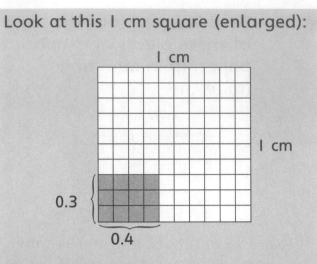

The length of the shaded portion is 0.4 cm (or 4 mm).

The breadth of the shaded portion is 0.3 cm (or 3 mm).

So, the area of the shaded portion is

0.4 cm × 0.3 cm

$= \dfrac{4}{10} \times \dfrac{3}{10}$ cm²

$= \dfrac{12}{100}$ cm²

$= 0.12$ cm²

But we can also find the answer by changing cm into mm, by multiplying, and finally dividing our answer by 100:

0.4 cm × 0.3 cm

= 4 mm × 3 mm

$= 12$ mm² $= \dfrac{12}{100}$ cm²

$= 0.12$ cm²

3. Work out the area of the shaded portion of each square, (i) in cm² and (ii) in mm².

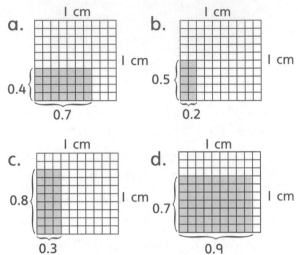

4. Complete these multiplications (i) by changing decimals into common fractions, (ii) by changing decimals into whole numbers, multiplying, then dividing your answer by 100.

0.5 × 1.7 ... (i) $\dfrac{5}{10} \times 1\dfrac{7}{10}$

$= \dfrac{5}{10} \times \dfrac{17}{10}$

$= 0.85$

(ii) $5 \times 17 = 85$

$85 \div 100 = 0.85$

a. 0.66 × 0.7   b. 7.1 × 1.9

c. 0.4 × 0.9   d. 6.4 × 0.8

e. 1.3 × 0.6   f. 3.7 × 2.4

Multiplying a Decimal Fraction by Hundredths

Look at this: 3.8×2.34

$$3.8 \times 2.34 = 3\frac{8}{10} \times 2\frac{34}{100}$$

$$= \frac{38}{10} \times \frac{234}{100}$$

$$= \frac{38 \times 234}{1000}$$

$$= \frac{8892}{1000}$$

$$= 8\frac{892}{1000} = 8.892$$

$$3.8 \times 2.34 = 8.892$$

1. Now, work out these multiplications.

   a. 2.4×1.58 b. 3.62×1.5
   c. 3.62×4.3 d. 7.6×4.84

Let us now see what happens if we change our decimal numbers into whole numbers.

$$3.8 \times 2.34$$

$$= \frac{38}{10} \times \frac{234}{100} = \frac{8892}{1000}$$

The two numbers have ③ decimal places. We divide 8892 by 1000. The answer will have 3 decimal places.

$$3.8 \times 2.34 = 8.892$$

2. Solve these by first changing decimal fractions into common fractions.

   a. 1.732×0.5 b. 0.482×1.9
   c. 2.415×1.4 d. 7.325×0.4
   e. 1.861×2.2 f. 4.09×7.3

When we solve multiplications like 0.172×3.6, we first change our decimal fractions into common fractions:

$$0.172 \times 3.6 = \frac{172}{1000} \times 3\frac{6}{10}$$

$$= \frac{172}{1000} \times \frac{36}{10}$$

$$= \frac{172 \times 36}{10000} = \frac{6192}{10000} = 0.6192$$

The answer will have 4 decimal places.

3. Copy and write denominators for *s. Then complete the sums.

   ★ $4.5 \times 3.2 = \frac{1440}{*} \ldots \frac{1440}{100} = 14.4$

   a. $1.62 \times 5.3 = \frac{8586}{*}$

   b. $3.8 \times 7.72 = \frac{29336}{*}$

   c. $8.45 \times 2.7 = \frac{22815}{*}$

4. Copy and write denominators in place of *s. Then multiply.

   ★ $1.4 \times 3.617 = \frac{50638}{*} \ldots \frac{50638}{10000}$
   $$= 5.0638$$

   a. $2.621 \times 0.7 = \frac{18347}{*}$ _____

   b. $0.939 \times 6.3 = \frac{59157}{*}$ _____

   c. $7.9 \times 8.64 = \frac{68256}{*}$ _____

   d. $0.68 \times 7.7 = \frac{5236}{*}$ _____

   e. $9.368 \times 5.2 = \frac{487136}{*}$ _____

OXFORD
UNIVERSITY PRESS

Dividing by a Decimal Fraction

When we divide a decimal fraction by a whole number, the quotient will have the same number of decimal places as the dividend:

Example A

$18.6 \div 3$

$= 18\dfrac{6}{10} \div \dfrac{3}{1}$

$= \dfrac{\cancel{186}^{62}}{10} \times \dfrac{1}{\cancel{3}}$

$= \dfrac{62}{10}$

$= 6.2$

(Keep '0's intact, in the denominator.)

Example B

$23.66 \div 14$

$= 23\dfrac{66}{100} \div \dfrac{14}{1}$

$= \dfrac{\cancel{2366}^{169}}{100} \times \dfrac{1}{\cancel{14}}$

$= \dfrac{169}{100}$

$= 1.69$

Sid, Selvi and Sara are now going to experiment with divisions where divisors are **decimal numbers**.

Sid has drawn a square 10 cm × 10 cm and divided it into 100 squares. He then colours 0.75 of his square (i.e., 75 little squares):

1 He now wants to cut his coloured portion into big squares, each with an area of 0.25 cm² (i.e., 25 little squares).

How many such squares can he make? Yes, 3. In effect, it asks, "How many quarters in one three-quarter of a whole?

0.75 cm² ÷ 0.25 cm² = 3

---

2 Selvi has a piece of ribbon 7.5 cm long. For her school project, she needs some strips of ribbon 2.5 cm long. How many pieces can she get from her 7.5 cm piece"?

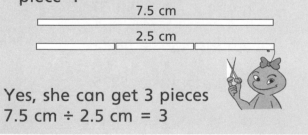

Yes, she can get 3 pieces
7.5 cm ÷ 2.5 cm = 3

3 Sara has a piece of green silk cloth 75 cm long. To make a dress for her doll, she needs some 25 cm long pieces. How many can she cut from her 75 cm length of cloth?

25 cm 25 cm 25 cm
———75 cm———

Yes, exactly 3 pieces.
75 cm ÷ 25 cm = 3

Let us look carefully at the answers to the experiments done by Sid, Selvi and Sara' on the previous page.

Sid's answer: $0.75 \div 0.25 = 3$

Selvi's answer: $7.5 \div 2.5 = 3$

Sara's answer: $75.0 \div 25.0 = 3$

All 3 experiments have the same answer! The three are **equivalent**.

$0.75 \div 0.25$ **is the same as**

$7.5 \div 2.5$, **which is the same as**

$75 \div 25$.

We know that when we divide decimal fractions, it is easy to do so when our divisor is a whole number.

$75 \div 25$ is simpler to solve than $0.75 \div 0.25$

What should we do, then, when we have $0.72 \div 0.6$?

Simple! **We change the divisor and the dividend into whole numbers.**

Multiply both the numerator and the denominator by 100

$$\frac{0.72}{0.6} \times \frac{100}{100} = \frac{72}{60} = 1.2$$

Answer: $0.72 \div 0.6 = 1.2$

1. Copy and complete the table.

	Division sum (decimal divisor)	Equivalent to (whole number divisor)	Answer
★	$1.8 \div 0.2$	$18 \div 2$	9
a.	$0.84 \div 0.12$		
b.	$21.9 \div 0.3$		
c.	$0.63 \div 0.21$		
d.	$0.85 \div 0.5$		

2. Look at the example and work out the divisions.

★ $0.64 \div 0.4$ $= \frac{0.64}{0.4} \times \frac{100}{100}$

$= \frac{64}{40} = 1.6$

a. $2.8 \div 0.7$ b. $0.49 \div 0.7$

c. $3.2 \div 0.8$ d. $9.5 \div 1.9$

e. $0.72 \div 0.9$ f. $0.55 \div 0.5$

Look at these:

a. $\frac{0.7}{0.14} = \frac{0.7}{0.14} \times \frac{100}{100} = \frac{70}{14} = 5$

b. $\frac{0.91}{0.013} = \frac{0.91}{0.013} \times \frac{1000}{1000}$

$= \frac{910}{13} = 70$

3. Now, work out these divisions.

a. $9.6 \div 0.048$ b. $556 \div 6.95$

c. $64.2 \div 1.07$ d. $0.9 \div 0.018$

Using Division to Change Common Fractions Into Decimal Fractions

Sprog and three of his friends want to share 3 cakes equally. How much for each space-boy?

3 cakes shared by 4 people = ?
or 3 ÷ 4 = ?

Remember 3.0 = 3.000

$$
\begin{array}{r}
0.75 \\
4\overline{)3.000} \\
28 \\
\hline
20 \\
20 \\
\hline
\end{array}
$$

So, $3 \div 4 = \dfrac{3}{4} = 0.75$

More examples: 1 chocobar and three boys or, 22 cakes and 7 boys!
i.e. 1 ÷ 3 or 22 ÷ 7
Remember: 1 = 1.0000

$$
\begin{array}{r}
0.3333 \\
3\overline{)1.0000} \\
9 \\
\hline
10 \\
9 \\
\hline
10 \\
9 \\
\hline
10 \\
9 \\
\hline
10 \\
\vdots
\end{array}
\qquad
\begin{array}{r}
3.14285 \\
7\overline{)22.000...} \\
21 \\
\hline
10 \\
7 \\
\hline
30 \\
28 \\
\hline
20 \\
14 \\
\hline
60 \\
56 \\
\hline
40 \\
35 \\
\hline
5 \\
\vdots
\end{array}
$$

They are both never ending!

1. Solve these.

   a. 5 ÷ 10   b. 6 ÷ 300   c. 7 ÷ 14

   Look at this:

   $$\frac{1}{8} = \frac{1.0000}{8}$$

   $$
   \begin{array}{r}
   0.125 \\
   8\overline{)1.000} \\
   8 \\
   \hline
   20 \\
   16 \\
   \hline
   40 \\
   40 \\
   \hline
   \end{array}
   $$

   So, $\dfrac{1}{8} = 0.125$

2. Now change these into decimal fractions.

   a. $\dfrac{1}{4}$ b. $\dfrac{3}{50}$ c. $\dfrac{7}{8}$

   d. $\dfrac{11}{20}$ e. $\dfrac{2}{5}$ f. $\dfrac{13}{25}$

3. Solve the following.

   a. While playing in the field, Sprog and his three friends find a ten-rupee note. They decide to divide the note among themselves. How much does each get?

   b. Spook gets a nice big chocolate on his birthday. At school he decides to share it with four of his friends. How much does each get?

Simplification with Decimal Fractions

Now that he knows how to use all four operations—addition, subtraction, multiplication and division for decimal fractions, Sid wants to put two or more operations together in the same sum. As before, he uses the DMAS rule to guide him:

$1.04 ÷ 0.2 × 6.3 = ?$
$= (1.04 ÷ 0.2) × 6.3$
$5.2 × 6.3$ **(divide first, multiply next)**
$= 32.76$
Answer: 32.76

1. Using the DMAS rule to guide you, simplify each expression.

a. $6.8 × 0.14 + 14.63$

b. $8.56 ÷ 0.08 + 2.4 − 1.72$

c. $10.01 × 3.5 − 6.881$

d. $0.95 ÷ 0.05 × 3.3$

e. $20.14 × 0.6 + 100.933$

NOW, BRACKET DANCE!

2. Simplify these.

★ $4.2 − \{6.85 − (4.72 − 1.68)\}$
$4.2 − \{6.85 − (3.04)\}$
$4.2 − \{6.85 − 3.04\}$
$4.2 − 3.81 = \textbf{0.39}$

a. $9.5 − (2.03 × 1.6)$

b. $7.41 + \{0.18 + (6.29 − 4.81)\}$

c. $(0.74 × 1.3) + (1.501 − 0.72)$

d. $4 × [0.7 + \{1.6 + 3.8 − (1.1 × 0.75)\}]$

e. $9.7 − \{6.38 − (18.17 − 14.39)\}$

f. $2 × [1.6 + \{33.9 − 2.4 + (0.3 × 0.4)\}]$

3. Copy and fill in the blanks.

a. $6.91 × 4.385$: the answer will have _____ decimal places.

b. To change 0.753 into a whole number, I must multiply by _____

c. $14.73 − 8.645 =$ _____

d. $6.49 ÷ 10 =$ _____

e. _____ $× 100 = 23.69$

f. $\dfrac{9}{20} =$ _____ in decimal form.

g. $6.2 × 3.85 =$ _____

h. $0.119 ×$ _____ $= 11.9$

OXFORD
UNIVERSITY PRESS

1. Rewrite these in decending order.

   a. 3.011, 3.101, 3.001, 3.301

   b. $\frac{28}{100}$, $\frac{3}{10}$, $\frac{8}{100}$, $\frac{500}{1000}$

2. Write vertically and complete.

   a. 6.841 − 13.962

   b. 482.04 + 75.938 + 1.2

3. Rewrite these groups of decimals as like decimals.

   4.058, 6.0, 7.29, 17.3

4. Work out the multiplications.

   a. 1.769 × 100   b. 1.3 × 7.9

   c. 72.034 × 24   d. 0.117 × 0.3

5. Work out the divisions.

   a. 115.02 ÷ 18   b. 0.42 ÷ 0.14

   c. 621.17 ÷ 100   d. 3.2 ÷ 0.04

6. Change these into decimal fractions.

   a. $\frac{3}{2}$ b. $\frac{15}{25}$ c. $\frac{13}{8}$

7. Solve these problems, making complete statements.

   a. Sprog Spacewalker has a strip of wood 52 cm long. For a model spaceship he is making, he needs small pieces of wood 2.6 cm long. How many can be cut from his long strip?

   b. How many 0.25-litre cups can be filled from a 4.5 l jug of lemonade?

   c. Sid Spacewalker finds 12.25 kg of flour in the cupboard. To bake one apple pie, he needs 1.75 kg of flour. How many pies can he bake?

   d. In the beginning of July, Sara Spacewalker weighed 51.25 kg. By the end of the month, she weighed 54.15 kg. How much weight had she gained?

   e. At an end-of-term party, 12 chocolate cakes are shared equally between 40 children. How much does each child get? Give your answer as a decimal fraction.

   f. The string attached to Sprog Spacewalker's kite is 20.65 m long. If Sprog lengthens it by 7.5 m, how long will the string be?

PART THREE

More about Rounding Off

Sid Spacewalker is in a bad mood! He has just received four bills and must pay them. To find out **quickly**, he decides to guess or estimate the total amount of money owed for each bill. Help him by ticking the **estimated** total which seems to be close to the **actual total**.
Work in your notebooks.

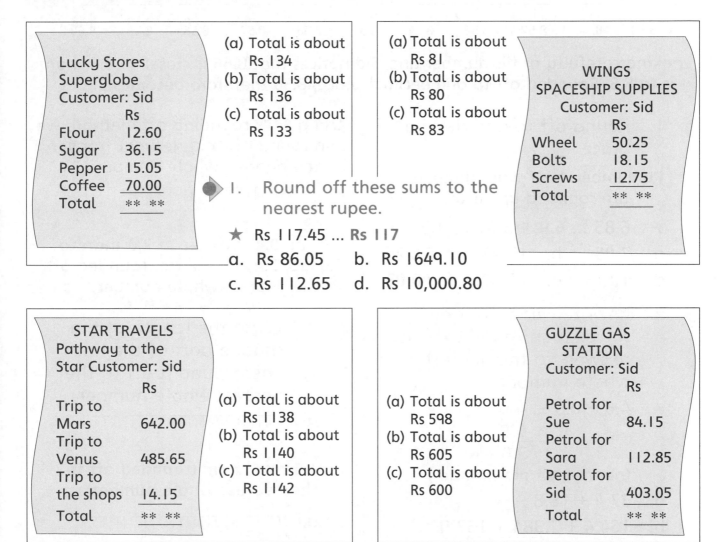

Lucky Stores		
Superglobe		
Customer: Sid		
		Rs
Flour		12.60
Sugar		36.15
Pepper		15.05
Coffee		70.00
Total		** **

(a) Total is about
Rs 134
(b) Total is about
Rs 136
(c) Total is about
Rs 133

(a) Total is about
Rs 81
(b) Total is about
Rs 80
(c) Total is about
Rs 83

WINGS		
SPACESHIP SUPPLIES		
Customer: Sid		
		Rs
Wheel		50.25
Bolts		18.15
Screws		12.75
Total		** **

1. Round off these sums to the nearest rupee.

★ Rs 117.45 ... **Rs 117**

a. Rs 86.05   b. Rs 1649.10

c. Rs 112.65   d. Rs 10,000.80

STAR TRAVELS	
Pathway to the	
Star Customer: Sid	
	Rs
Trip to	
Mars	642.00
Trip to	
Venus	485.65
Trip to	
the shops	14.15
Total	** **

(a) Total is about
Rs 1138
(b) Total is about
Rs 1140
(c) Total is about
Rs 1142

(a) Total is about
Rs 598
(b) Total is about
Rs 605
(c) Total is about
Rs 600

GUZZLE GAS	
STATION	
Customer: Sid	
	Rs
Petrol for	
Sue	84.15
Petrol for	
Sara	112.85
Petrol for	
Sid	403.05
Total	** **

Add up the four answers you have ticked to find out Sid's approximate total expenses. If he has Rs 2000 in his bank account, will he able to pay all his bills?

Just as we can round off decimal numbers to the nearest whole number, we can round off decimals with **2 decimal places** (with **tenths** and **hundredths**) to a decimal fraction with just **1 decimal place** (that is, written to the **nearest tenth only**).

Sid wants to round off 8.56 to the nearest tenth (or to 1 decimal place). He draws a number line to help him work it out:

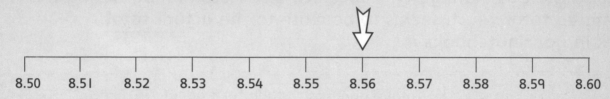

Looking carefully at his number line, Sid notices that 8.56 is closer to 8.6 than it is to 8.5. **Rounded off to one decimal place, 8.56 therefore becomes 8.6.**

1. Round off to one decimal place.

    Remember: half-way numbers are rounded upwards.

    ★ 6.85 ... 6.9;   3.01 ... 3.0

    a. 7.05   b. 15.43   c. 26.25

    d. 10.15   e. 27.07   f. 40.03

2. Rewrite vertically and solve. Then round off your answers to the nearest whole number.

    ★ 4.6 − 0.8 ... 4.6
    $$\begin{array}{r} 4.6 \\ -\,0.8 \\ \hline 3.8 = 4 \end{array}$$
    (nearest whole number)

    a. 37.4 + 16.8

    b. 164.4 + 2.384 + 162.9

    c. 1003.5 − 869.9

    d. 142.9 + 238.6 + 14.7

    e. 2061.4 − 1453.8

Using Sid's rounding off method, we can round off any decimal fraction to the nearest whole number:

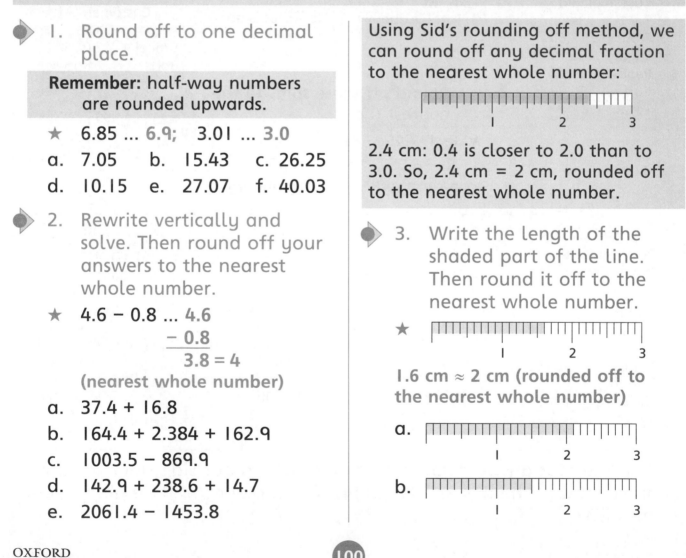

2.4 cm: 0.4 is closer to 2.0 than to 3.0. So, 2.4 cm = 2 cm, rounded off to the nearest whole number.

3. Write the length of the shaded part of the line. Then round it off to the nearest whole number.

    ★

    1.6 cm ≈ 2 cm (rounded off to the nearest whole number)

    a.

    b.

Rounding Off with Decimals: to 2 Decimal Places

When Sid works out the details of his space journey (for example, how much fuel he will need for every km travelled), he decides to simplify his work by rounding off all numbers with 3 decimal places to numbers with 2 decimal places. This is how he does it:

0.326 +
10.895
÷ 6.983
× 4.817
× 1000

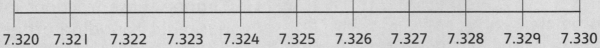

7.320 7.321 7.322 7.323 7.324 7.325 7.326 7.327 7.328 7.329 7.330

Sid remembers his rule: half-way numbers are rounded upwards.
So he knows that a 5, 6, 7, 8, or 9 in the thousandths column means that the number should be rounded upwards. If the number in the thousandths column is less than 5, the number should be rounded downwards.

Example:
7.322 = 7.32 (to 2 decimal places), 7.326 = 7.33 (to 2 decimal places)

1. Round off to 2 decimal places.

   ★ 8.015 ... **8.02**

   a. 6.132   b. 14.109

   c. 2.494   d. 148.003

   e. 8.027   f. 1792.007

2. Rewrite vertically and solve. Then round off your answer to 2 decimal places.

   a. 10.049 + 3.117 + 8.632

   b. 28.032 − 14.595

   c. 94.128 + 13.3 + 6.497

   d. 72.064 − 18.967

   e. 52.135 − 29.772

3. Multiply or divide, then round off your answer to 2 decimal places.

   a. 4.3 × 6.21

   b. 38.15 × 7.8

   c. 24.18 × 5.7

   d. 4.9 ÷ 0.7

   e. 14.4 ÷ 1.8

   f. 32.1 ÷ 10.7

Rounding off is a very useful maths tool, and one which we use often. It helps us simplify calculations which would otherwise be very complicated.

Look at this example:

$$\frac{1}{8} = 0.125$$

This is simple,

But look what happens if we try to change $\frac{1}{3}$ into a decimal.

As we did earlier, we divide the numerator by the denominator:

$$
\begin{array}{r}
0.333 \\
3{\overline{)}\,1.000} \\
9 \\
\hline
10 \\
9 \\
\hline
10 \\
9 \\
\hline
1..
\end{array}
$$

Do you see what is happening? We are getting the same remainder again and again, while the digit 3 in the quotient is appearing again and again. We have a **recurring decimal!**

So, how do we express $\frac{1}{3}$ as a decimal? We write it like this:

$$\frac{1}{3} = 0.3333333333... \text{ or } 0.\dot{3}$$

But that looks very clumsy, and makes calculations difficult. Instead, we can round off our numbers to a few places of decimal:

$\frac{1}{3} =$ 0.333 (to 3 decimal places)

or 0.33 (to 2 decimal places)

or 0.3 (to 1 decimal place)

◆ 1. Change these fractions into decimals, rounding off your answers to 3 decimal places.

a. $\frac{19}{9}$ b. $\frac{10}{3}$ c. $\frac{19}{3}$

d. $\frac{16}{6}$ e. $\frac{16}{7}$ f. $\frac{29}{7}$

In other cases, our division may not give us the same recurring digit in the quotient, but a string of different digits which go on and on. There is no exact answer.

Example: $\frac{1}{7}$

$$\frac{1}{7} = 0.14285...$$

= 0.143, to 3 decimal places, or 0.14, to 2 decimal places.

$$
\begin{array}{r}
0.14285 \\
7{\overline{)}\,1.00000} \\
7 \\
\hline
30 \\
28 \\
\hline
20 \\
14 \\
\hline
60 \\
56 \\
\hline
40
\end{array}
$$

◆ 2. Change these into decimals, rounding off your answer to 3 decimal places.

a. $\frac{1}{6}$ b. $\frac{4}{11}$ c. $\frac{3}{7}$

d. $\frac{2}{3}$ e. $\frac{13}{3}$ f. $\frac{8}{9}$

Once we know how to round numbers off to a few decimal places, we can express any quotient as a decimal number, rather than a quotient with a remainder.

For example, 47,321 ÷ 56
There are two methods:

Method I

```
        845 r1
    56) 47321
        448
        252
        224
        281
        280
          1
```

Answer: 845 r 1

Method 2

```
          845.0178
    56) 47321.0000
        448
        252
        224
        281
        280
        100
         56
        440
        392
        480
        448
         32..
```

Answer:

845.018 (to 3

decimal places)

Remember:

To give our answer to 3 decimal places, we continue dividing till we have 4 places of decimals. Then we round off.
So, the answer = 845.018

1. Solve these divisions, rounding off your answers to 2 decimal places.

   a. 15,623 ÷ 49

   b. 472,689 ÷ 64

   c. 78,309 ÷ 62

   d. 508,933 ÷ 72

2. Now solve these, rounding off your answers to 3 decimal places (Remember: keep dividing till you have four places of decimals, then round off).

   a. 53,997 ÷ 48

   b. 78,632 ÷ 145

   c. 90,455 ÷ 67

   d. 65,339 ÷ 281

recurring

OXFORD
UNIVERSITY PRESS

Percentages: a Special Kind of Fraction

Sprog Spacewalker is working on his maths homework. He is looking carefully at 5 squares divided into different fractions. What part of the square is coloured in each case?

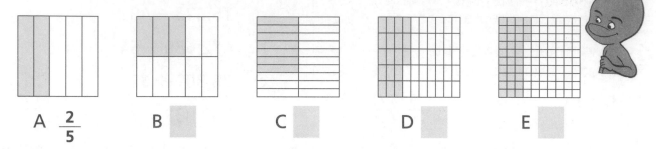

A $\frac{2}{5}$ B ▢   C ▢   D ▢   E ▢

Next, Sprog wants to arrange the squares in ascending order, according to the fraction coloured.

Sprog finds this difficult. How can he compare **unlike fractions**: that is, fractions with different denominators?

This can be done by drawing smaller squares, so that they all have the same number of small squares (i.e., the same denominator). 100, as a common denominator, is a good choice, and Sprog divides his squares thus, keeping the same area of each square coloured:

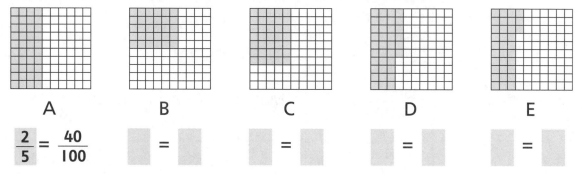

A   B   C   D   E

$\frac{2}{5} = \frac{40}{100}$ ▢ = ▢   ▢ = ▢   ▢ = ▢   ▢ = ▢

Any fraction with 100 as a denominator can be expressed as a percentage.

For example, $\frac{40}{100} = 40\%$, $\frac{30}{100} = 30\%$ and so on.

Fill in the boxes by counting the shaded squares.

Sprog now finds it easy to arrange his squares in **ascending order** according to their coloured area.

Can you also rank the squares in ascending order?

Write your sequence here: _____, _____, _____, _____, _____

Here are Sprog's results in the form of a table:

Name of square	Fraction coloured	=	Fraction coloured
A	$\frac{2}{5}$	=	$\frac{40}{100}$
B	$\frac{3}{10}$	=	$\frac{30}{100}$
C	$\frac{7}{20}$	=	$\frac{35}{100}$
D	$\frac{18}{50}$	=	$\frac{36}{100}$
E	$\frac{33}{100}$	=	$\frac{33}{100}$

In each case, the fraction on the left has been changed into an **equivalent fraction with the denominator 100.**

1. Change these fractions into equivalent fractions with denominator 100.

   ★ $\frac{15^{\times 5}}{20^{\times 5}} = \frac{75}{100}$

   a. $\frac{7}{10}$ b. $\frac{9}{10}$ c. $\frac{4}{5}$

   d. $\frac{1}{5}$ e. $\frac{11}{25}$ f. $\frac{21}{25}$

2. Express these as fractions of 100, rounding off to 2 decimal places where necessary.

   ★ $\frac{2}{11}$ of $100 = \frac{100 \times 2}{11} = \frac{200}{11}$
   $= 18.18$ (to 2 decimal places)

   a. $\frac{4}{7}$ of 100 b. $\frac{11}{14}$ of 100

   c. $\frac{3}{16}$ of 100 d. $\frac{2}{19}$ of 100

Sprog's teacher has asked him to colour $\frac{1}{3}$ of this hundred square. $\frac{1}{3}$ of 100 is 33 whole squares and $\frac{1}{3}$ more.

How do we work this out?

$$\frac{1}{3} = \frac{?}{100}$$

Sprog uses 2 different methods to find the answer:

Method 1 (common fraction notation):

$$\frac{1}{3} = \frac{1}{3} \times \frac{100}{100}$$
$$= \frac{100}{3} \times \frac{1}{100} = 33\frac{1}{3}$$

So, $100 = 33\frac{1}{3}\%$

$$3\overline{\smash{)}100}\ \ ^{33\ r\ 1}$$
$$\underline{9}$$
$$10$$
$$\underline{9}$$
$$1$$

Method 2 (decimal notation):

$$\frac{1}{3} = \frac{1}{3} \times \frac{100}{100}$$
$$= \frac{100}{3} \times \frac{1}{100}$$
$$= 33.33\%$$

$$3\overline{\smash{)}100.}\ \ ^{33.33..}$$
$$\underline{9}$$
$$10$$
$$\underline{9}$$
$$10$$
$$\underline{9}$$
$$1..$$

OXFORD
UNIVERSITY PRESS

For the last few pages, we have been helping Sprog to change different fractions into equivalent fractions with the denominator 100!

In modern English, we use the word 'hundred' to describe this number. This word came into the English language a very long time ago. It first arrived with invaders from Germany and Scandinavia, who used word like **'hundred'** and **'hundert'** to express the idea of 100. ... With use, the word gradually changed...

Hundert km to London

But, of course, in other parts of the world, 100 has had quite different names.
In ancient Rome, the Latin word for 100 was *centum*. The first letter of the word gave the symbol **C**, used in the Roman numeral system.

ROMA 'C' km

Some of the words we use in modern English are based on the Latin word 'centum'. For example, century, which means:
(a) a period of 100 years

MOZART THE 18th CENTURY

or (b) a batsman's score of 100 runs in a cricket match!

SCORE 100

Here are some more words we use today, all of them based on the Latin word 'centum':

Centenary	100th birthday or anniversary
Cent	a small coin used in the USA and other countries and equal to $\frac{1}{100}$ of a dollar
Centipede	literally, **'one hundred feet'**: if you count the feet of this insect, you may find as many as 100!

Another modern word which is based on the Latin word centum is percentage. A percentage is a special kind of fraction. It always has a denominator of **100**.

$$1\% = \frac{1}{100}, 2\% = \frac{2}{100}, 11\% = \frac{11}{100} \text{ and so on}$$

Also $\frac{2}{10} = \frac{20}{100} = 20$ **per cent**

$\frac{3}{25} = \frac{12}{100} = 12$ **per cent**

$\frac{1}{8} = \frac{12\frac{1}{2}}{100} = 12\frac{1}{2}$ **per cent**

1. Write each fraction as a percentage.

   ★ $\frac{36}{100}$ ... **36 per cent**

   a. $\frac{7}{10}$ b. $\frac{1}{4}$ c. $\frac{3}{8}$

   d. $\frac{19}{100}$ e. $\frac{9}{10}$ f. $\frac{1}{6}$

% This symbol means "per cent" or "upon 100".

We use it like this:

$\frac{44}{100}$ = 44 per cent = 44%

$\frac{53}{100}$ = 53 per cent = 53%

Have you noticed something interesting about this symbol? It contains all the numerals in 100, but jumbled up.

100 → 0 / 0

2. Write each fraction as a percentage, using the special symbol.

   ★ $\frac{18}{50}$ ... $= \frac{36}{100} = 36\%$

   a. $\frac{7}{10}$ b. $\frac{99}{100}$ c. $\frac{30}{50}$

   d. $\frac{8}{10}$ e. $\frac{3}{5}$ f. $\frac{8}{25}$

3. Write each percentage as a fraction, reducing it to its lowest terms where possible

   ★ $25\% \ldots = \frac{25}{100} = \frac{1}{4}$

   a. 30%   b. 45%   c. 89%

   d. 24%   e. 32%   f. 100%

4. Change these fractions into percentages, rounding off your answers to 2 decimal places where necessary:

   ★ $\frac{1}{9} \ldots \frac{1}{9} \times \frac{100}{100} = \frac{100}{9} \times \frac{1}{100}$
   $= 11.11\%$

   a. $\frac{2}{7}$ of 100   b. $\frac{5}{14}$ of 100

   c. $\frac{5}{9}$ of 100   d. $\frac{6}{13}$ of 100

   e. $\frac{3}{13}$ of 100   f. $\frac{2}{15}$ of 100

OXFORD
UNIVERSITY PRESS

Using Percentages

If we remember that a percentage is simply a special kind of fraction whose denominator is **always** 100, we can change any common fraction or decimal fraction into a percentage.

Let us first look at how we change common fractions, mixed numbers and whole numbers into percentages.

We already know how to change a common fraction like this into a percentage:

$$\frac{5}{7} = \frac{5}{7} \times \frac{100}{100}$$

$$= \frac{500}{7} \times \frac{1}{100}$$

$$= 71.429\ \% \text{ (to 3 decimal places)}$$

How do we change a mixed number like this?

$$2\frac{3}{4}$$

$$2\frac{3}{4} = \frac{11}{4}$$

$$= \frac{11}{4} \times \frac{100}{100} = \frac{1100}{4}\% = 275\%$$

Also, because 4 is a factor of 100, we can change the fraction $\frac{11}{4}$ into an equivalent fraction with denominator 100:

$$\frac{11^{\times 25}}{4^{\times 25}} = \frac{275}{100} = 275\%$$

1. Change these mixed numbers into percentages.

★ $3\frac{1}{5} \ldots = \frac{16}{5} \times \frac{100}{100}$

$= \frac{1600}{5} \times \frac{1}{100} = 320\%$

a. $4\frac{1}{4}$ b. $6\frac{7}{20}$ c. $6\frac{3}{50}$

d. $1\frac{3}{5}$ e. $3\frac{4}{5}$ f. $8\frac{7}{10}$

It is very simple to change whole numbers into percentages. We just follow the same steps, turning our whole number into fraction form:

$4 = 4 \times \frac{100}{100} = 400 \times \frac{1}{100} = 400\%$

2. Change these into percentages.

a. 6   b. 17   c. 58
d. 9   e. 23   f. 79

In the case of decimal numbers, however, it is a different story. For example:

$6.79 = 6.79 \times \frac{100}{100} = 679 \times \frac{1}{100} = 679\%$

Short cut!
Just shift the decimal point to the right by two places! You get the percentage!

3. Change these into percentages.

a. 0.23   b. 7.394   c. 7.01
d. 4.69   e. 3.9   f. 3.00

Change percentages into decimal or common fractions:

$$65\% = \frac{65}{100} = 0.65$$

Also, $\quad 65\% = \frac{65}{100} = \frac{13}{20}$

$$180\% = \frac{180}{100} = \frac{18}{10} = 1.8$$

Also, $\quad 180\% = \frac{180 \div 20}{100 \div 20} = \frac{9}{5} = 1\frac{4}{5}$

$$500\% = \frac{500}{100} = 5.0$$

Also, $\quad 500\% = \frac{500}{100} = \frac{5}{1} = 5$

4. Change these percentages into fractions, mixed numbers or whole numbers, reducing where you can.

   a. 75%   b. 300%   c. 21%

   d. 38%   e. 135%   f. 800%

How do we change a percentage into a decimal?

Let us take 39% and show it on a hundred square:

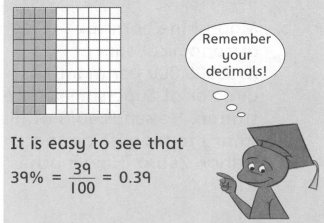

Remember your decimals!

It is easy to see that

$$39\% = \frac{39}{100} = 0.39$$

5. Change these percentages into decimal numbers.

   ★ 24% ... $= \frac{24}{100} = 0.24$

   a. 35%   b. 1.8%   c. 98%

   d. 140%   e. 6%   f. 16.3%

6. Change these decimal numbers into percentages:

   ★ 0.05 ... $= \frac{5}{100} = 5\%$

   a. 0.39   b. 0.6   c. 1.0

   d. 0.04   e. 0.55   f. 1.52

7. Copy and complete Sid's table.

Sara's Performing % Percentages %

%	Fraction with denominator	Decimal	Fraction in lowest terms
50%	$\frac{50}{100}$	0.50 or 0.5	$\frac{1}{2}$
10%			
1%			
			$\frac{2}{1}$ or 2
		4.55	
	$\frac{175}{100}$		

Using Percentages

In Galaxy Departmental Store near Sid Spacewalker's house, the following items are on special reduction during a sale:

Thermos flask
Rs 80
10% off

Plastic bucket
Rs 65
20% off

'Supastripe' toothpaste
Rs 12.50
5% off

'Klik-it' camera
Rs 800
15% off

Sid wants to work out how much each item will cost after the special reduction:

Thermos flask : Special reduction

$= 10\%$ of Rs $80 = \dfrac{10}{100} \times$ Rs 80

$= $ Rs $\dfrac{800}{100} = $ Rs 8

Price is reduced by Rs 8.
Special price $= $ Rs $80 - $ Rs $8 = $ Rs 72

8. Look at the price board. Help Sid by working out the special price of:

   a. the plastic bucket
   b. the 'Klik-it' camera
   c. the toothpaste

9. Calculate each percentage of the quantity given.

★ 20% of 650 km

$= \dfrac{\overset{1}{\cancel{20}}}{\underset{5}{\cancel{100}}} \times \overset{130}{\cancel{650}}$ km

$= 130$ km

   a. 10% of Rs 50
   b. 10% of 75 g
   c. 50% of 1000 km
   d. 12% of 600 l
   e. 7.5% of 60 m

10. Solve, making complete statements.

   a. Mrs Shah earns Rs 8500 every month from her work as a computer operator. If her boss gives her a 10% increase in salary, how much will she now earn every month? And how much will she earn in one year?

   b. Moonshine earns an astronomical sum of Rs 3,500,000 per month as director of Supershine space station. He sends 40% of his salary to his wife on space station Zebra. How much is that?

Percentages are useful in understanding and comparing information quickly and easily. Turn back to page 104. As soon as Sprog changed all his squares into **hundredths** and showed his coloured areas as **percentages**, it was easy for him to compare and rank them. Look at this newspaper clipping:

MULTAN, 30 September, A census by students has found that 11 out of 25 people living in Central Lane are office workers. In Sunset Street, 21 out of 44 residents are office workers.

It is not easy for us to compare the information given here. We are not sure which of the two streets has the higher fraction of office workers. But if we turn the information into percentage, it will become easy to compare:

Central Lane	Sunset Street
$\dfrac{11}{25} \times \dfrac{\overset{4}{\cancel{100}}}{100}$	$\dfrac{21}{44} \times \dfrac{100}{100}$
$= \dfrac{44}{1}\%$	$= \dfrac{2100}{44}\%$
$= 44\%$	$= 47.73\%$

We can, therefore, rewrite the newspaper article thus:

MULTAN, 30 September, A census by students has found that 44% of people living in Central Lane are office workers. In Sunset Street, 47.73% are office workers.

It is now clear.

11. Rewrite these newspaper stories, changing fractions into percentages.

a. Superglobe, 14 January
   24 out of 48 cows on Moon View arm are suffering from toothache. On Space Field farm, 32 out of 60 cows are suffering from the same complaint.
b. Tauland, 27 March
   On yesterday's rocket-bus from Superglobe, 240 out of 500 seats were occupied. On the bus from Tauland to Venus, 325 out of 600 seats were occupied.

12. Now solve these, making complete statements.

a. In her end-of-term exams, Salima got 33 out of 50 marks in Urdu and 7 out of 10 marks in History. What were her two marks in percentages? In which subject did she do better?

b. In a TV quiz programme, Sid answers 65 questions and gets 32 answers right. Sara answers 80 questions and gets 56 correct answers. Give their scores in percentages and find out who is better at quizzes!

Profit and Loss

Shopkeepers and other business people use percentages in their work. When shopkeepers sell you an item, they hope to get **more money** than they have paid for that item. They hope to make a **profit**. Sid's friend Steve Stargazer is a rocket salesman:

He has just bought a rocket for Rs 8000. He hopes to sell it to a customer of his for Rs 10,000. How much **profit** will he make?

To find the answer, we subtract the cost price (C.P.) from the selling price (S.P.):

S.P.	=	Rs 10000
C.P.	=	− Rs 8000
Profit	=	Rs 2000

▶ 1. Work out Steve's profit on each of these rocket sales.

★ C.P. = Rs 14,500 ... Rs 16000
S.P. = Rs 16,000 − Rs 14500
Profit = Rs 1500   Rs 1500

a. C.P. = Rs 13,250
S.P. = Rs 15,800

b. S.P. = Rs 30,000
C.P. = Rs 24,075

c. C.P. = Rs 8900
S.P. = Rs 12,450

d. C.P. = Rs 12,450
S.P. = Rs 14,700

Like every businessperson, Steve wants to **compare** one sale with another. For which sales has he made a higher **proportion** of profit?

He finds that out by changing his profit into a **percentage profit**. For the rocket bought for Rs 8000 and sold for Rs 10,000, the percentage profit will be:

$$\frac{Rs\ 2000}{Rs\ 8000} \times 100\%$$

$$= \frac{\overset{1}{2000}}{\underset{4}{8000}} \times 100\%$$

$$= \frac{100}{4}\% = 25\%$$

Profit = 25%

RULE
$$Profit\ \% = \frac{Profit}{Cost\ price} \times 100$$

▶ 2. Work out the percentage profit on these sales.

★ C.P. = Rs 5000
Profit = Rs 2500 ...

$$Profit = \frac{\overset{1}{2500}}{\underset{2}{5000}} \times 100 = \frac{100}{2} = 50\%$$

Profit = 50%

a. C.P. = Rs 6000
Profit = Rs 1200

b. C.P. = Rs 4500
Profit = Rs 1500

c. C.P. = Rs 850
Profit = Rs 90

d. C.P. = Rs 565
Profit = Rs 50

OXFORD
UNIVERSITY PRESS

Steve Stargazer does not always succeed in making a profit. Last year, for example, he bought what seemed to be a very good rocket for Rs 7500. But when Steve looked at it more closely, he found that the engine was bad and that the bodywork was badly scratched.

Steve was able to sell the rocket for only Rs 6000 (S.P.).

    C.P. = Rs 7500
    S.P. = Rs 6000

The S.P. was much less than the sum he had paid for it (C.P.). There was **a loss** on the sale.

How much did he lose? To find out, we subtract the selling price (S.P.) from the cost price (C.P.):

    C.P. =   Rs 7500
    S.P. = − Rs 6000
    ─────────────────
    Loss =   Rs 1500

3. Work out Steve's loss on each of these sales.

★ C.P. = Rs 3600...   Rs 3600
  S.P. = Rs 1950   − Rs 1950
                      ─────────
                       Rs 1650

  Loss = Rs   1650

a. C.P. = Rs   4700
   S.P. = Rs   3850
b. S.P. = Rs   7225
   C.P. = Rs 10,000
c. C.P. = Rs 16,500
   S.P. = Rs 14,750

Steve hates to make a loss! He especially hates making big losses. But how do you tell a big loss from a small one?

Once again, Steve makes use of **percentages** to work out the sales in which he has a higher **loss proportion**:

C.P. = Rs 7500, S.P. = Rs 6000,
Loss = Rs 1500

$$\text{Loss}\% = \frac{Rs\ 1500}{Rs\ 7500} \times 100$$
$$= \frac{1500}{7500} \times 100$$
$$= \frac{100}{5} = 20\%$$

The percentage loss on this sale = 20%

RULE $\text{Loss}\% = \dfrac{\text{Loss}}{\text{Cost price}} \times 100\%$

4. Work out (i) the loss; (ii) the percentage loss on these sales.

★ C.P. = Rs 1000 ...   Rs 1000
  S.P. = Rs 800   − Rs   800
                      ─────────
        Loss =   Rs   200

  $\%\text{Loss} = \dfrac{200}{1000} \times 100$
  $= \dfrac{200}{10} = 20\%$

a. C.P. = Rs 2500
   S.P. = Rs 2000
b. S.P. = Rs 3250
   C.P. = Rs 4500
c. C.P. = Rs 7250
   S.P. = Rs 6000

OXFORD
UNIVERSITY PRESS

Profit and Loss

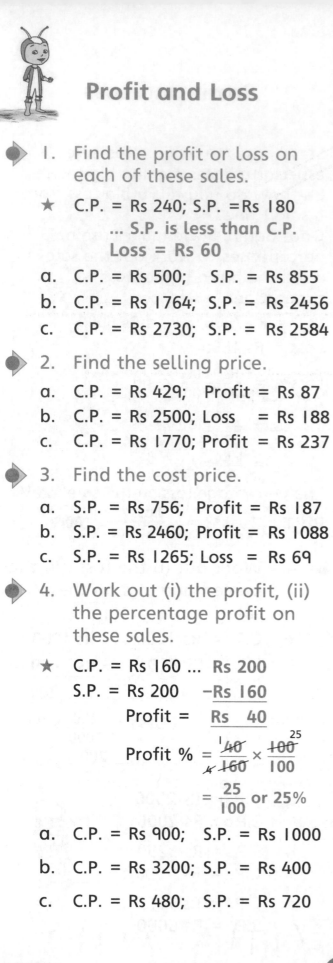

1. Find the profit or loss on each of these sales.

    ★ C.P. = Rs 240; S.P. =Rs 180
       ... S.P. is less than C.P.
       Loss = Rs 60

    a. C.P. = Rs 500;   S.P. = Rs 855
    b. C.P. = Rs 1764; S.P. = Rs 2456
    c. C.P. = Rs 2730; S.P. = Rs 2584

2. Find the selling price.

    a. C.P. = Rs 429;   Profit = Rs 87
    b. C.P. = Rs 2500; Loss   = Rs 188
    c. C.P. = Rs 1770; Profit = Rs 237

3. Find the cost price.

    a. S.P. = Rs 756; Profit = Rs 187
    b. S.P. = Rs 2460; Profit = Rs 1088
    c. S.P. = Rs 1265; Loss = Rs 69

4. Work out (i) the profit, (ii) the percentage profit on these sales.

    ★ C.P. = Rs 160 ... Rs 200
       S.P. = Rs 200   −Rs 160
              Profit =   Rs   40

       $\text{Profit \%} = \dfrac{\overset{1}{40}}{\underset{4}{160}} \times \dfrac{\overset{25}{100}}{100}$

       $= \dfrac{25}{100}$ or 25%

    a. C.P. = Rs 900;   S.P. = Rs 1000
    b. C.P. = Rs 3200; S.P. = Rs 400
    c. C.P. = Rs 480;   S.P. = Rs 720

5. Find the profit or loss as a percentage of the cost price.

    ★ Sara buys a TV for Rs 8000. She later sells it for Rs 6500.

       C.P   = Rs 8000
       S.P. = Rs 6500
       Loss = Rs 1500 %

       $\text{Loss \%} = \dfrac{1500}{80\cancel{00}} \times \dfrac{1\cancel{00}}{100}$

       $= \dfrac{1500}{80} \% = \dfrac{150}{8} \%$

       Loss % = 18.75%

    a. Sid bought a motorcycle for Rs 7000. After three accidents, he sold it for Rs 4500.

    b. The Jamal's bought a refrigerator for Rs 20,000. Five years later they sold it for Rs 27,500.

    c. At Wholesale Cloth Centre, Alam buys cotton cloth at Rs 50 per metre. He sells it to his customers at Rs 75 per metre.

    d. Rehan bought a cycle for Rs 2600. After using it for a year, he sold it for Rs 2200.

    e. Adil buys apples for his stall at Rs 40 per dozen. He sells them at Rs 56 per dozen.

MONEYBAGS BANK

Planet City Branch

Sid Spacewalker has a **bank account** at the Planet City branch of Moneybags Bank. This allows him to keep the money in a safe, secure place, in addition he earns interest on it.

When Sid **deposits** (puts) money in his bank account, the bank is very pleased. It uses Sid's money, perhaps lending it to another customer who needs money to build a home or start a business.

Of course, if Sid wants to **withdraw** (take out) some or all of his money, the bank will let him do so.

The bank pays Sid some extra money as a kind of thank you, because it **makes use** of Sid's money. We call this extra money **interest**.

Sid's uncle Sam also has a bank account with Moneybags Bank. Sam wants to

expand his business. He needs a lot of money to do this. So he meets his **bank manager** (the person in charge of the bank) and asks for a **bank loan**.

The bank manager agrees, but reminds Sam that he will have to pay back not only the amount of the loan but also some extra money as a 'thank you' to the bank for lending the money. This **extra money**, too, is called **interest**.

Go and visit the bank nearest to your school, and find out how much interest they will give you if you deposit money with them. It is good to learn to save money!

Simple Interest

The money Sid Spacewalker puts into his bank account is called the **principal**. The extra money, or **interest**, Sid gets from the bank for keeping his money there will be a **percentage** of his principal, usually paid once every year.

So at the end of a year, Sid's bank account will show a larger **amount**:

Look at this:
Principal = Rs 5000
Rate of Interest = 10%
Time = 1 year

∴ Amount = Principal + Interest in 1 year

$$= Rs\ 5000 + \frac{10}{100} \times Rs\ 5000$$
$$= Rs\ 5000 + Rs\ 500$$
$$= Rs\ 5500$$

The sum of money Sam Spacewalker **borrows** from the bank is called the **principal**. The extra money, or **interest**, which Sam must pay the bank for the use of the money will also be a **percentage** of the principal. Sam will have to pay it at the end of the year, or at some other specified time. At the end of the year, the money Sam owes the bank will show a larger **amount**.

Look at this:
Principal (P) = Rs 10,000
Interest (I) = 15%

$$A = P + I$$
$$= Rs\ 10000 + \frac{15}{100} \times Rs\ 10000$$
$$= Rs\ 10000 + Rs\ 1500$$
$$= Rs\ 11500$$

1. Work out the amount in these bank accounts after one year.

   ★ Principal = Rs 2000
      Interest = 5%
      Amount = P + I
      $$= Rs\ 2000 + \frac{5}{100} \times Rs\ 2000$$
      $$= Rs\ 2000 + Rs\ 100$$
      $$= Rs\ 2100$$

   a. Principal = Rs 3000
      Interest = 20%
   b. Principal = Rs 1000
      Interest = 7.5%
   c. Principal = Rs 600
      Interest = 15%

2. Work out the amount owed to the bank after one year.

   ★ Principal = Rs 4500
      Interest = 9%
      Amount = P + I
      $$= Rs\ 4500 + \frac{9}{100} \times Rs\ 4500$$
      $$= Rs\ 4500 + Rs\ 405$$
      $$= Rs\ 4905$$

   a. Principal = Rs 12,000
      Interest = 6%
   b. Principal = Rs 20,000
      Interest = 12.5%
   c. Principal = Rs 18,500
      Interest = 8%

OXFORD
UNIVERSITY PRESS

The longer the period for which Sid keeps his money in the bank without withdrawing it, the more interest he will earn.

If Sid keeps his principal of Rs 5000 in the bank for 1 year, and is paid 10% interest on it, the amount in his account will grow to Rs 5500. But see what happens if Sid only withdraws the interest but keeps his money undisturbed for longer periods:

Principal	Rate of Interest	Amount after 1 year	Amount after 2 years	Amount after 3 years
Rs 5000	10%	Rs 5000 + Rs 500 = Rs 5500	Rs 5000 + (Rs 500×2) = Rs 6000	Rs 5000 + (Rs 500×3) = Rs 6500

The interest Sid earns therefore depends on three factors:

a. The size of his principal (P)

b. The **rate** (percentage) of interest (R)

c. The period of deposit, i.e. Time (T)

Sid uses a simple formula to calculate how much interest he will earn:

$$\text{Interest} = \text{Principal (P)} \times \frac{\text{Rate (R)}}{100} \times \text{Time (T)}$$

For example:

if Sid plans to keep his principal of Rs 5000 in the bank for $3\frac{1}{2}$ years, then total interest will be:

$$= \text{Rs Principal} \times \frac{\text{Rate}}{100} \times \text{Time}$$

$$= \text{Rs } 50\cancel{00} \times \frac{10}{1\cancel{00}} \times 3\frac{1}{2}$$

$$= \text{Rs } 50 \times 10 \times \frac{7}{2}$$

$$= \text{Rs } 1750$$

Interest = Rs 1750 in $3\frac{1}{2}$ years

$$= \text{Rs } 500 \text{ a year for } 3\frac{1}{2} \text{ years.}$$

3. Calculate the interest where:

★ Principal (P) = Rs 600

Rate (R) = 9%

Time (T) = 4 years

$$\text{Interest} = \frac{P \times R \times T}{100}$$

$$= \text{Rs } \frac{600 \times 9 \times 4}{100}$$

$$= \text{Rs } 216$$

a. P = Rs 100
R = 3%
T = 3 years

b. P = Rs 1500
R = 8%
T = 5 years

OXFORD
UNIVERSITY PRESS

c. P = Rs 250
   R = 4%
   T = 5 years

d. P = Rs 2000
   R = 7.5%
   T = 3 years

e. P = Rs 12,000
   R = 6%
   T = 4 years

f. P = Rs 28,750
   R = 5%
   T = $5\frac{1}{2}$ years

g. P = Rs 25,000
   R = 12%
   T = 6 years

h. P = Rs 16,600
   R = 14%
   T = 2 years

i. P = Rs 2400
   R = 15%
   T = 4 years

4. Work out these problems.

a. Mick Moon deposits Rs 4000 in a bank account for his daughter Meg. How much money will be in the account after 5 years if the bank pays Mick a $12\frac{1}{2}$ % rate of interest?

b. Mrs Siddiqui deposits Rs 3000 in a **fixed deposit account**. She agrees not to withdraw any money before 3 years are over. In return, the bank will pay her a 16% rate of interest. How much interest will Mrs Siddiqui earn during this period? How much money will be in her account at the end of 3 years?

1. Round off to 2 decimal places.

   a. 18.494 b. 143.099 c. 475.199

2. Change into decimals, rounding off to 3 decimal places.

   a. $\frac{4}{9}$ b. $\frac{6}{7}$ c. $\frac{14}{15}$

3. Write as percentages (to 2 decimal places, if necessary)

   a. $\frac{7}{20}$ b. $2\frac{2}{9}$ c. 0.51

   d. $\frac{8}{25}$ e. $4\frac{4}{7}$ f. 1.2

   g. $\frac{8}{9}$ h. 8   i. 1.032

4. Write as fractions in their lowest terms:

   a. 28%   b. 72%   c. 600%

5. Change into decimals.

   a. 48%   b. 2.5%   c. 142%

6. Calculate:

   a. 40% of Rs 480

   b. 75% of 600 l

   c. 5% of 7000 km

7. Work out the price of these items on special offer.

   a. Softy Soap: 10% off on Rs 5.50

   b. Transistor radio: 20% off on Rs 260

   c. School bag: 15% off on Rs 125

8. Calculate the interest payable where.

   a. P = Rs 300
       R = 4%
       T = 6 years

   b. P = Rs 7500
       R = 11%
       T = 9 months
       ($\frac{3}{4}$ years)

   c. P = Rs 2500
       R = $7\frac{1}{2}$%
       T = 3 years

   d. P = Rs 3600
       R = 14%
       T = $2\frac{1}{4}$ years

9. Solve these problems.

   a. Sue Spacewalker borrows Rs 7550 to buy a space-moped. The bank asks her to pay the money back over 3 years at 15% rate of interest. Find (i) the interest she must pay, and (ii) the total amount of money she must repay at the end of 3 years.

   b. Which of these bank customers will earn the largest sum of interest every year?

   (i) Usman: P = Rs 6000, R = 7%
              T = 4 years

   (ii) Zeba: P = Rs 4500, R = $8\frac{1}{2}$%
                T = 10 years

   (iii) Rashid: P = Rs 7250, R = 6%
                 T = 2 years

OXFORD
UNIVERSITY PRESS

Remembering Angles

1. Sid remembers that there are five different types of angles, but he can't remember their names. Help him complete the crossword by naming each angle shown in the clues.

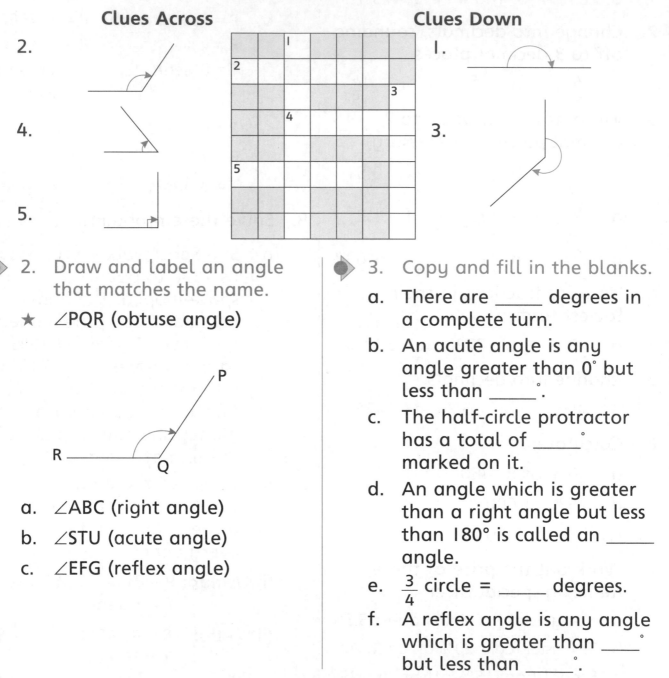

Clues Across

2.

4.

5.

Clues Down

1.

3.

2. Draw and label an angle that matches the name.

   ★ ∠PQR (obtuse angle)

   a. ∠ABC (right angle)
   b. ∠STU (acute angle)
   c. ∠EFG (reflex angle)

3. Copy and fill in the blanks.

   a. There are _____ degrees in a complete turn.
   b. An acute angle is any angle greater than 0° but less than _____°.
   c. The half-circle protractor has a total of _____° marked on it.
   d. An angle which is greater than a right angle but less than 180° is called an _____ angle.
   e. $\frac{3}{4}$ circle = _____ degrees.
   f. A reflex angle is any angle which is greater than _____° but less than _____°.

Find right angles, acute angles and obtuse angles in your classroom. Make a list and compare it with your friends.

4. Use your protractor to measure these angles. Think carefully which row of markings on the protractor you should use.

a.

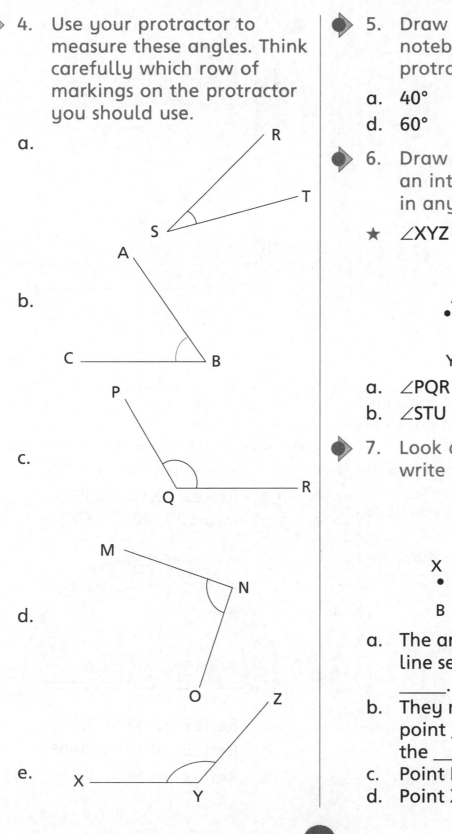

b.

c.

d.

e.

5. Draw these angles in your notebook, using a protractor.

a. 40°   b. 90°   c. 55°
d. 60°   e. 115°   f. 145°

6. Draw these angles adding an interior or exterior point in any suitable place.

★ ∠XYZ = 80°; exterior point A

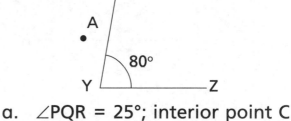

a. ∠PQR = 25°; interior point C
b. ∠STU = 115°; exterior point J

7. Look at this angle. Then write words in the blanks.

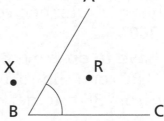

a. The angle is made up of two line segments, _____ and _____.

b. They meet at a common point _____ which is called the _____.

c. Point R is in the _____ .

d. Point X is in the _____ .

Using the Protractor: Reflex Angles

Look at this reflex angle:

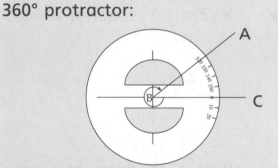

How do we use our protractor to measure it?

It's simple if we have a circular, 360° protractor:

By centring our protractor along line segment BC, we can easily see that reflex ∠ABC = 320°.

But, to measure a reflex angle using a half-circle protractor, we remember our rule: one complete turn = 360°.

All we have to do is measure the acute ∠ABC, and subtract that number from 360° to get reflex ∠ABC.

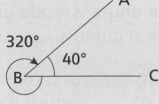

Here, **acute** ∠ABC = 40°
∴ reflex ∠ABC = 360° − 40°
              = 320°

1. Calculate these reflex angles, using your protractor.

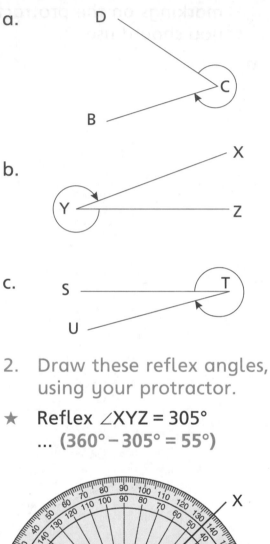

a.

b.

c.

2. Draw these reflex angles, using your protractor.

★ Reflex ∠XYZ = 305°
   ... (360° − 305° = 55°)

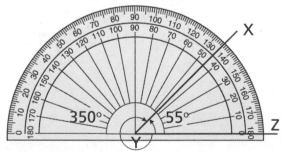

a. Reflex ∠PQR = 320°
b. Reflex ∠WXY = 290°
c. Reflex ∠CDE = 335°

Using the Protractor: Compass and Bearings

Sid's brother, Stan Spacewalker, is the captain of a ship which sails the sixteen seas of Superglobe. When Captain Stan takes his ship, the Golden Cockroach, out to sea, he needs to know **in which direction** he must sail to reach his destination.

To do this, Captain Stan uses a special instrument called a

compass (say 'kum-puss'). At first sight, the compass looks rather like a clock. It is circular and has one moving hand.

But instead of numerals, it has four letters of the alphabet marked on it, one for each of the four basic directions: **N**orth, **S**outh, **E**ast and **W**est.

Whichever way Stan turns the compass, the long hand keeps pointing along the original direction.

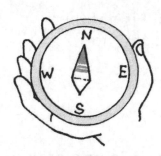 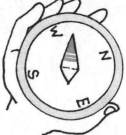 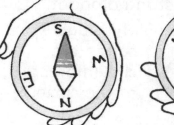 

The direction to which the long hand **always** points is **North**.

Compass

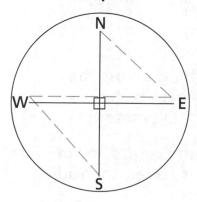

The compass is very similar to a circular protractor. The angle between each of the 4 compass points is **90°** or one right angle.

Circular protractor

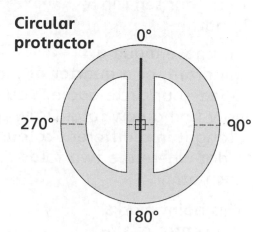

Did you know?

The four letters for the four directions give us the word NEWS if you form the letter Z, beginning at N .

OXFORD
UNIVERSITY PRESS

More about Circles

A complete turn has 360°.

The shape made by one complete turn is the shape of a circle.

Look at Sara's fan, now fully opened to make a circle.
If we measure each fold of her fan, from the centre to the edge, we find that the length stays the same.

A circle is the path of a moving point which is always at the **same distance from a fixed point.**

centre

Let's now find out more about circles and their special features:

1

Using a small plate, or the base of a tumbler or bottle, draw a circle on a piece of paper and cut it out. Run your finger round its edge. Stick a string along it.

This edge is called the **circumference** of the circle.

2

Now fold your circle in half: Each half of the circle is called a **semicircle**.

semi-circle

('Semi' is another word for 'half'.)

3

Open up your circle and draw a coloured line along the fold:

diameter

This line stretching across the middle of the circle is the **diameter** (say 'die-ameter').

The line from the centre to the circumference is called the **radius** (say 'ray-dee-us').

Diameter = 2 × Radius

4

Fold your circle back in half along the diameter fold. Then fold your semicircle in half.

quadrant

You have made a **quadrant**, or a quarter of a circle. Open your circle again. You will now find a new fold. Draw a line along it in a different colour. Mark a dot where the two folds cross each other.

This point marks the **centre** of the circle:

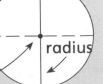
radius

1. Measure the diameter of each circle.

★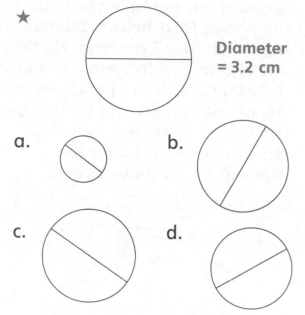
Diameter = 3.2 cm

a.

b.

c.

d.

Now look at this circle:

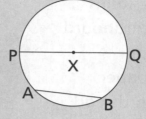

It has two line segments, PQ and AB, cutting across it. Both line segments are called **chords**.

Line PQ passes through the centre of the circle, X. So it is also called the **diameter**.

Line AB does not pass through the centre of the circle. It is simply a **chord**.

2. Now calculate the radius of each circle in Exercise 1.

★ Diameter = 3.2 cm

Radius = $\frac{3.2}{2}$ cm = 1.6 cm

3. Complete these.

a. If a circle has a diameter of 9.64 cm, its radius will be _____ cm.

b. If the radius of a circle equals 5.845 m, its diameter is _____ m.

c. A quarter circle is also known as a _____ .

d. The diameter of a circle always passes through the _____ of the circle and joins together 2 points on its _____ .

4. Using a small plate or the bottom of a tumbler, draw a circle in your notebook. Mark a point on its circumference and label it A.

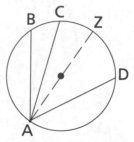

Draw as many chords as possible, using point A as one of the end points. Make one of your chords pass through the centre of your circle. Label your chords (AB, AC, AD, etc.) and measure each of them. Which is the longest of the chords you have drawn?

OXFORD
UNIVERSITY PRESS

Making Circles: Using Compasses

To make an accurate circle, Sid collects these items:
- a piece of cardboard
- a drawing pin
- a sheet of paper
- some cotton thread
- a pencil
- pair of compasses

1

Sid glues his sheet of paper onto the cardboard. He then sticks his drawing pin firmly in the middle of the paper. Next he cuts a length of thread about 15 cm long. He ties one end to the drawing pin and the other end to his pencil. Holding the pencil upright and pulling on the thread to keep it taut, Sid moves the pencil **round** the drawing pin to draw a **circle**:

2

Sid looks inside his instrument box and finds something which looks rather like his pencil and pin gadget:

3

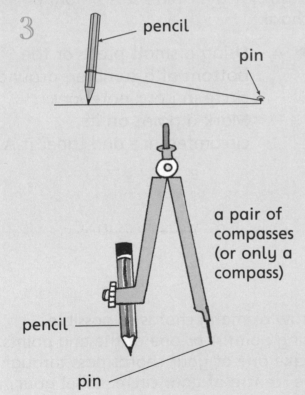

pencil

pin

a pair of compasses (or only a compass)

pencil

pin

Work with this like you did with the pencil and pin gadget to draw a circle.

Sid takes another sheet of paper. He places the 'pin' or the pivot of his compass in the middle of it. He extends the pencil arm about 3 cm away from the pivot. He then carefully walks the pencil arm round the pivot. He makes a **perfect circle!**

4

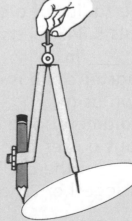

OXFORD
UNIVERSITY PRESS

Making Circles: Using Compasses

Look how Sid stretches the compasses to 3.5 cm on a ruler.

A pair of compasses is referred to as "a compass" in everyday English.

To draw the circle Sid puts the pivot (pin) of the compasses on the point which he wants to be the centre. He then holds the handle at the top and slowly twists it, so that the pencil hand slowly slides on the paper. He has to take care that the pin is not displaced from the centre while drawing the circle. Now, practise it several times.

1. Using your ruler and compasses, draw circles with these radii (radii—say 'ray-dee-eye'—is the plural form of radius).

    a. 4 cm   b. 7 cm   c. 3.3 cm
    d. 5 cm   e. 4.5 cm   f. 4.1 cm

2. Without using your ruler, state the diameter of each of the circles you have drawn in Exercise A.

    ★ Circle a: radius = 4 cm
    ∴ diameter = 8 cm

This is how Sid draws the circle. Here, Sid has drawn only part of the circumference of a circle:

When we draw or refer to only **part** of a circle's circumference, we call that part an **arc**.

Arcs can be of many sizes:

even a **semicircle** like this....
We usually name an arc of a circle by means of **three points**:

Arc ABC or Arc AXC

3. Look at this circle.

    a. Name **all** the radii of the circle.
    b. Measure the lengths of the diameters.
    c. Name **all** the arcs marked on the circumference.

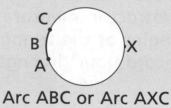

OXFORD
UNIVERSITY PRESS

More about Triangles

Here is Sid's check-list of facts about triangles:

1. Triangles are all about threes: each triangle has **3** sides, **3** vertices and **3** angles.

2. Triangles can be grouped into types or categories according to their sides or according to their angles:

Grouping by Sides	Grouping by Angles
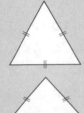 3 equal sides: **equilateral triangle**	one angle right angle: **right-angled triangle** 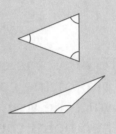
2 equal sides: **isosceles triangle**	all 3 angles acute: **equilateral triangle**
all sides of different length: **scalene triangle**	one angle an obtuse angle: **obtuse-angled triangle**

1. Measure the sides of this triangle with your ruler. Record your findings in the table. Then, with your protractor, measure the angles of the triangle and record your findings.

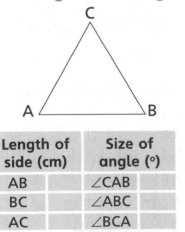

Length of side (cm)		Size of angle (°)	
AB		∠CAB	
BC		∠ABC	
AC		∠BCA	

What type of triangle is this? What do you observe about its angles?

2. Now measure and record the sides and angles of this triangle.

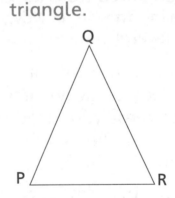

Length of side (cm)		Size of angle (°)	
PQ		∠RPQ	
QR		∠PQR	
PR		∠QRP	

What type of triangle is shown? What do you notice about its angles?

3. Measure and record the sides and angles of this triangle.

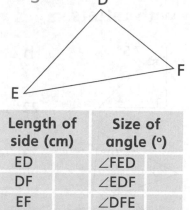

Length of side (cm)		Size of angle (°)	
ED		∠FED	
DF		∠EDF	
EF		∠DFE	

What type of triangle is this?
What is special about its angles?

We can now add these points to Sid's checklist:

Equilateral △s

All 3 sides are of the same length. All 3 angles are also equal.

Isosceles △s

2 sides are of the same length. 2 angles are of the same size.

Scalene △s

The length of each side is different. The size of each angle is also different.

Notice the special symbol, △, we use for a triangle. We also have special symbols to show equal lengths and equal angles: study the drawings.

4. Measure each triangle (sides and angles), then name the triangle family to which it belongs. Present your findings in the form of a table.

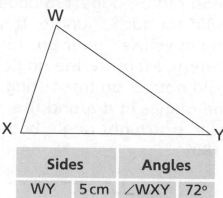

Sides		Angles	
WY	5 cm	∠WXY	72°
YX	5 cm	∠XWY	72°
XW	3 cm	∠WYX	36°

△ Family = isosceles

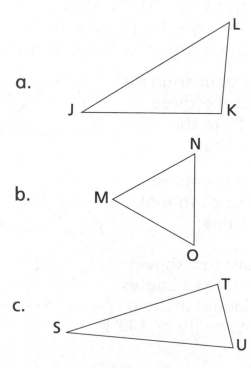

a.

b.

c.

OXFORD
UNIVERSITY PRESS

More about Triangles

Sid remembers one more important fact about triangles:

The sum of the angles of a △ is always 180°.

Check back to see that the angles you measured on page 128 added up to 180° for each triangle. If not, you may have used your protractor inaccurately. Measure the angles again. Sid notices an interesting link: The angles in a △ and the degrees in a straight angle **both equal 180°.**

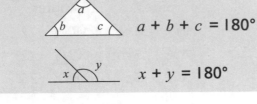

$a + b + c = 180°$

$x + y = 180°$

5. Take a blank sheet of paper or cardboard. Draw a triangle on it, and mark each angle with dots, thus.

Cut out your triangle, then cut the three angles from the triangle thus:

Arrange the three angles so as to make a straight line:

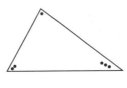

You have just shown how the three angles of a triangle make a straight angle or 180°!

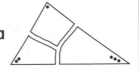

6. Without using your protractor, calculate the size of the angles marked with letters.

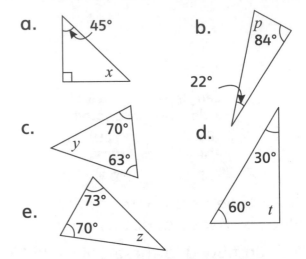

a. 45°

x

b. p

84°

22°

c. 70°

y

63°

d. 30°

e. 73°

70°

z

60° t

7. Here is a page from Sprog Spacewalker's geometry notebook. He has measured the angles of some △s, but not very carefully. Make a list of the triangles whose angles have been measured incorrectly.

Triangles

a. $\angle ABC = 90°$ b. $\angle CDE = 25°$
$\angle BAC = 70°$ $\angle CED = 115°$
$\angle ACB = 20°$ $\angle DCE = 43°$

c. $\angle POR = 110°$ d. $\angle JLK = 85°$
$\angle PRO = 40°$ $\angle JKL = 45°$
$\angle RPO = 40°$ $\angle KJL = 40°$

e. $\angle STU = 35°$ f. $\angle XYZ = 35°$
$\angle SUT = 47°$ $\angle XZY = 110°$
$\angle TSU = 100°$ $\angle ZXY = 40°$

Constructing Triangles

We can construct a triangle if we know:

      (a) the length of all **3 sides**

or (b) the length of **2 sides** plus the size of the angle between them

or (c) the size of **2 angles** plus the length of the sides between them

To construct a triangle when all **3 sides are given**:
for example, △ABC where AB = 5 cm, AC = 4 cm and CB = 3 cm.

Step 1

With ruler and pencil, draw
line AB (5 cm).

A ├──────────────── B
        5 cm

Step 2

Keeping the pivot of your compasses
on the 0 cm mark, stretch out the
pencil arm till the pencil point
touches the 4 cm mark. Now place the
pivot on point A of line AB. Mark an
arc with your compass.

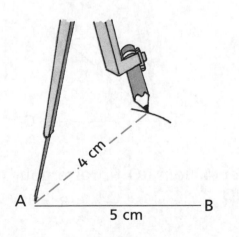

Step 3

Readjust your compasses so that the
arms are 3 cm apart (use your ruler!)
Place the pivot on point B and draw a
second arc:

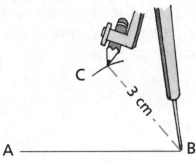

Step 4

The point where the two arcs cross
marks the third vertex, C, of your
triangle. Join C to A and then to B,
using your ruler.

You have constructed △ABC!

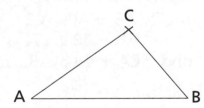

1. Construct these triangles,
using your ruler and
compass.

    a. △ ABC: AB = 6 cm, AC =
3 cm and CB = 4 cm

    b. △ PQR: PQ = 7 cm, QR =
5 cm and PR = 4 cm

    c. △ RST: RS = 9 cm, ST =
7.5 cm and RT = 3 cm

OXFORD
UNIVERSITY PRESS

Sprog wants to construct a triangle with sides 5 cm, 2 cm and 2 cm. Look at his construction:

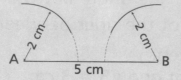

The two arcs will never cross, so the third vertex of the triangle cannot be constructed. Now, make each arc at a distance of 3 cm.

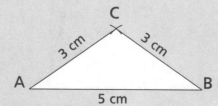

The two arcs cross: this is an isosceles triangle.

Sprog notes an interesting pattern: when any two sides in a triangle are added together, their length is greater than the third side.

In his triangle, AB + AC > CB
$$AB + CB > CA$$
and CA + CB > AB.

2. Tick the sets of measurements which cannot be made into triangles.

a. 3 cm, 2 cm, 4 cm
b. 8 cm, 4 cm, 1 cm
c. 4 cm, 11 cm, 8 cm

Sid now demonstrates how to construct a triangle when 2 sides and the angle between them are given:

△PQR where PQ = 4 cm, PR = 4 cm and ∠RPQ = 40°.

Step 1 Draw line PQ (4 cm).

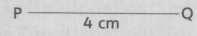

Step 2 Place your protractor so that it is exactly centred on point P. Mark a 40° angle. Then join this point O to P.

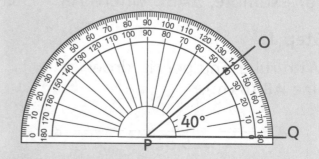

Step 3 Extend your compasses to exactly 4 cm. With the pivot on point P, mark an arc. The point where the arc crosses the straight line OP gives you point R, the third vertex.

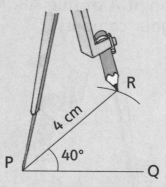

Step 4 Join RQ to form your triangle PRQ.

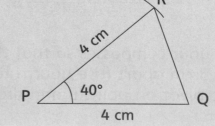

3. Construct these triangles.

    a. △XYZ where XY = 6 cm, XZ = 4 cm and ∠YXZ = 50°

    b. △EFG where EF = 5.5 cm, EG = 4.5 cm and ∠GEF=65°

    c. △RST where RS = 4.8 cm, RT = 6.5 cm and ∠TRS = 35°

Finally, Sid shows how to construct a triangle when we know 2 angles plus the length of the side between them.

His example: △ WXY where ∠XWY = 50°; ∠WXY = 45° and side WX = 3.5 cm.

Step I Draw line WX = 3.5 cm long. Draw a second straight line at an angle of 50° from the point W:

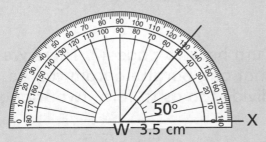

Step 2 Now construct angle WXY (45°), again drawing a straight line:

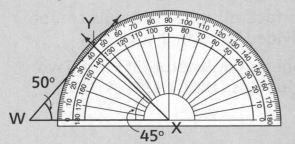

The point where the two lines cross is the third vertex, Y of △WXY.

4. Now construct these triangles.

    a. △PQR where ∠QPR = 30°, ∠PQR = 60° and side QP = 4 cm

    b. △ABC where side AB = 5 cm, ∠BAC = 45° and ∠ABC = 25°

    c. △JKL where ∠KJL = 65°, ∠JKL = 40° and side JK = 4.6 cm

    d. △TUV where ∠UTV = 80°, ∠TUV = 25° and side TU = 8 cm

5. Construct the triangles whose measurements are given in this table.

	AB	BC	∠ABC
a.	5 cm	2.5 cm	75°
b.	5.6 cm	3 cm	115°
c.	4.8 cm	5.2 cm	35°

6. Now construct triangles with these measurements.

	AB	∠CAB	∠CBA
a.	4.5 cm	45°	75°
b.	5.6 cm	25°	55°
c.	6.3 cm	90°	35°

7. Choosing your own measurements, construct and then label.

    a. any equilateral triangle

    b. any isosceles triangle

    c. any scalene triangle

Remembering Quadrilaterals

1. Complete the crossword.

Clues Across

1. The _____ sides of rectangles are of equal length.
4. The shape with 4 equal sides and 4 right angles.
5. The name of this shape:

6. The shape with 4 equal sides but no right angles.
7. If my sides are 2 cm, 4 cm, 2 cm and 4 cm and all my angles are 90° each, I'm called a _____

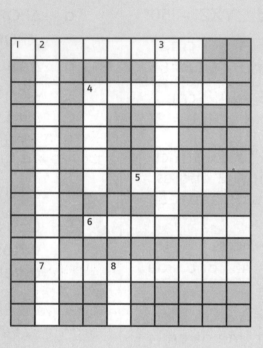

Clues Down

2. The name of this shape:
3. The name of this shape:
4. If three angles of a quadrilateral add up to 300°, the fourth angle will be _____ degrees.
8. If three of a kite's sides equal 3 cm, 3 cm and 10 cm, the fourth side will equal _____ cm.

2. Name each of these quadrilaterals. Then measure all 4 angles. What is the sum of the angles?

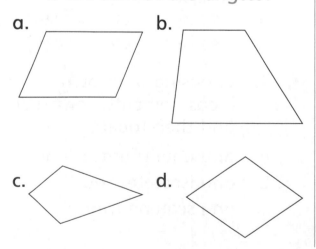

Turn back to page 42. There we saw that any parallelogram can be divided so as to form two triangles:

In fact, all quadrilaterals can be divided to form 2 triangles.

One quadrilateral (360°) = Two triangles (180° + 180° = 360°)

Sid remembers that when one line is at right angles to another ...

(i)

A

B □—— C

or crosses another line at right angles

P   B

(ii)   A   Q

... we say that the two lines are **perpendicular** to each other.

In figure (i), line AB is **perpendicular** to line BC.

In figure (ii), line PQ is **perpendicular** to line AB.

1. In the following figure, some of the coloured lines are perpendicular to line PQ. Write their names in your notebook.

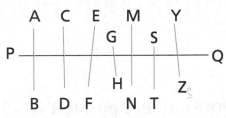

2. Study this figure, then complete the sentences.

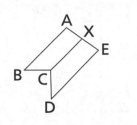

a. AB is perpendicular to _____

b. AE is perpendicular to _____

c. DE is perpendicular to _____

d. XC is perpendicular to _____

Remember the word we use for two or more lines that will never meet?

They are called **parallel lines**.
Parallel lines will never meet, however far we extend them. Here are some examples of parallel lines we see every day:

Bars in a window (to keep thieves away!)

Lines in your notebook (to keep it neat!)

Railway tracks (and the sleepers in between)

3. Look carefully at line XY. Which of the lines are parallel to the coloured line? Write their names in your notebook.

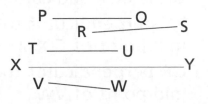

OXFORD
UNIVERSITY PRESS

Constructing Perpendicular and Parallel Lines

When we draw a line **perpendicular** to another line, we use our protractor or our set square to draw a right angle.

Let's first draw line CA **perpendicular** to the end point of line AB, using our protractor:

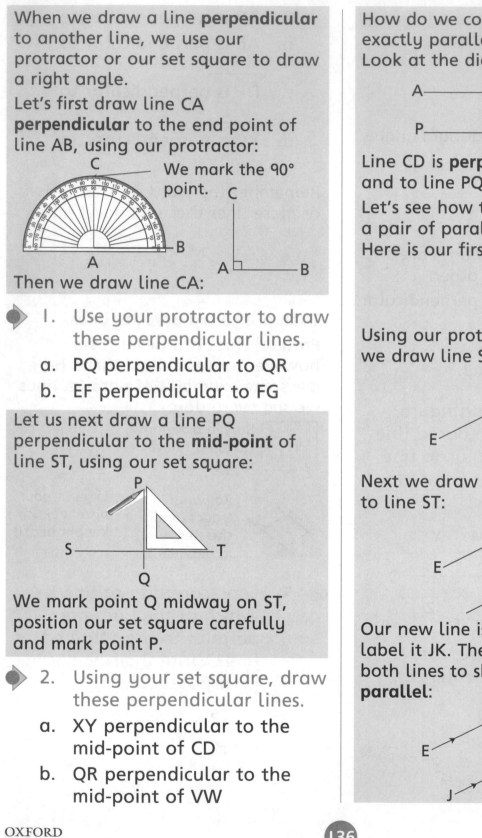

We mark the 90° point.

Then we draw line CA:

1. Use your protractor to draw these perpendicular lines.

   a. PQ perpendicular to QR

   b. EF perpendicular to FG

Let us next draw a line PQ perpendicular to the **mid-point** of line ST, using our set square:

We mark point Q midway on ST, position our set square carefully and mark point P.

2. Using your set square, draw these perpendicular lines.

   a. XY perpendicular to the mid-point of CD

   b. QR perpendicular to the mid-point of VW

How do we construct lines which are exactly parallel to one another? Look at the diagram below.

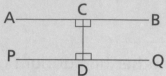

Line CD is **perpendicular** to line AB and to line PQ.

Let's see how this helps us construct a pair of parallel lines, EF and JK Here is our first line, EF:

Using our protractor or set square, we draw line ST **perpendicular** to it:

Next we draw a line **perpendicular** to line ST:

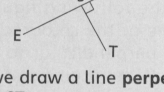

Our new line is **parallel** to EF! We label it JK. Then we mark **arrows** on both lines to show that they are **parallel**:

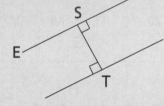

More about Parallel Lines

1. Using your ruler and protractor (or set square), draw these sets of parallel lines. Do not forget to mark arrows on them.

   ★ Line AB parallel to line CD, 1 cm apart

   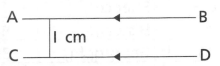

   a. Line JK parallel to line LM, 3.5 cm apart

   b. Line CD parallel to line EF, 4.2 cm apart

2. Now draw these, following the instructions carefully.

   ★ Parallel lines PQ and RS, each 3.8 cm long, and 1.7 cm apart

   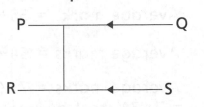

   a. Parallel lines AB and CD, each 4.1 cm long, and 3.4 cm apart

   b. Parallel lines OP and QR, each 5.6 cm long, and 1.7 cm apart

So far we have been looking at parallel lines which happen to be **straight** lines. But lines do not have to be straight in order to be parallel. Look at this diagram:

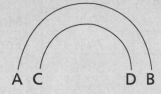

It shows **2 curved lines**, **AB** and **CD**. Both of them form arcs of a circle. Even without measuring, we can see that the 2 lines run parallel to each other, the distance between them always being the same.

We can construct parallel curved lines by using our compasses. We keep the pivot on the same point, X, and adjust the pencil arm to different lengths:

Circles which share the same centre but are of different radii are called **concentric** circles. Their circumferences are **parallel** to one another. Where do you see concentric circles around you? Look at a dart board.

   a. Draw two concentric circles, one of radius 2 cm and the other of radius 3.5 cm.

   b. Draw three concentric circles of radii 1.7 cm, 2.6 cm and 4.5 cm.

OXFORD
UNIVERSITY PRESS

Thinking about Averages

Sprog's class teacher, Ms Selena Startrek, is working on her end-of-term report cards. Here are the exam results of three of her students:

Class 5B Sprog	
Maximum marks in each subject: 100	
Maths	92%
English	74%
Science	68%
History	22%
Geography	58%
Urdu	16%
Comments:	

Class 5B Bop	
Maximum marks in each subject: 100	
Maths	75%
English	43%
Science	100%
History	49%
Geography	53%
Urdu	64%
Comments:	

Class 5B Jip	
Maximum marks in each subject: 100	
Maths	86%
English	64%
Science	72%
History	90%
Geography	30%
Urdu	88%
Comments:	

Ms Startrek wants to find out which of these students have done the best work, overall. She first adds up the total marks each student has got:

Sprog gets 92 + 74 + 68 + 22 + 58 + 16 = 330 marks

Bop gets 75 + 43 + 100 + 49 + 53 + 64 = 384 marks

Jig gets 86 + 64 + 72 + 90 + 30 + 88 = 430 marks

From this, Ms Startrek sees that Jig has got the highest **total** marks. She now divides each total by the number of subjects (the number of addenda) to arrive at the **average** marks scored by each student:

RULE

To find the average of a set of quantities, add them together, then divide the total by the number of addenda.

Sprog: $\frac{330}{6}$ Average marks = 55%

Bop: $\frac{384}{6}$ Average marks = 64%

Jig: $\frac{430}{6}$ Average marks = 71.666...%
= 71.7% to 1 decimal place

▶ 1. Work out the average of these sets.

★ 12, 6, 21, 13   **Total = 52**
                   Addenda = 4
                   Average = 13

a. 14, 27, 5, 19, 10

b. Rs 36, Rs 14, Rs 17, Rs 42, Rs 101

c. 8 cm, 25 cm, 15 cm, 32 cm, 10 cm

▶ 2. Copy and complete these.

a. The average of 1, 2, 3, 4 and 5 is____.

b. The average of 10, 100 and 1,000 is ____.

c. To find the average of 18, 14, 5, and 7, we divide ____ by 4.

Averages help us make sense of the information and data we see all around us.

For example, a doctor may wish to know the height of children aged 10 years. He can do this by measuring and writing down the heights of some children:

Rabia   145 cm
Saher   147 cm
Ayesha   148 cm
Arif   150 cm
Maria   143 cm

There is a difference in height between Maria and Arif, despite the fact that they are of the same age. The data is not very useful to the doctor until he works out the average:

$$\frac{\text{Total height}}{\text{No. of children}} = \frac{733 \text{ cm}}{5} = 146.6 \text{ cm}$$

The doctor gets the useful information that the **average height** of children aged 10 is 146.6 cm. He can then see which children are **above** average height and which children are **below** average height.

3. Below are the weights recorded for four 10-year-old children. Work out the average weight of the children.

Name	Weight
Mona	34.0kg
Kashif	36.2kg
Aslam	35.8kg
Insia	40.0kg

4. Solve these word problems, making complete statements.

a. Sid buys a kilogram of space-fingers on 6 different days. The prices he pays are Rs 8, Rs 10, Rs 7.50, Rs 12, Rs 11.75 and Rs 9.25. Find the average price.

b. Over a 4-month period, Moiz's monthly income was Rs 5000, Rs 4000, Rs 2500 and Rs 1000. What was his average income for that period?

c. Study this table: it shows the number of girls and boys studying at Ahsan Primary School:

Class	Girls	Boys
LKG	24	18
UKG	21	23
1	26	20
2	25	19
3	18	26
4	20	24
5	27	21

Find (i) the average number of girls in each class, (ii) the average number of boys in each class, (iii) the total number of children in the school and (iv) the average number of children in each class.

OXFORD
UNIVERSITY PRESS

Averages and Graphs

1. This column graph shows one week's attendance for Class 5 at Ahsan Primary School.

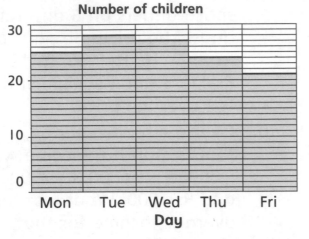

Number of children

Study the graph, then work out:

a. The total attendance for each day of the week.

b. The **average** daily attendance.

c. On which days the attendance was below the average.

2. This column graph shows the marks (out of 20) scored by 6 children in a spelling test.

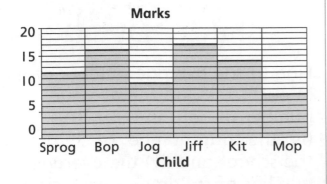

Marks

Study the graph, then work out the average marks scored by the 6 children. Which children scored above the average?

This graph shows the price of 4 storybooks:

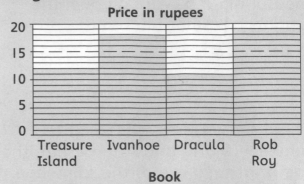

Price in rupees

The dotted line shows the average price of the 4 books.

You can see that the average is a number roughly **halfway between** the smallest number and the largest number.

3. Here is the top part of a column graph showing 4 children's results in a test.

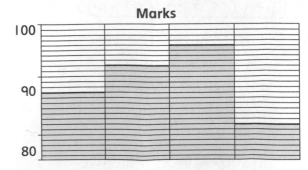

Marks

Look at the graph and **estimate** what the average marks will be. Then work out the average **exactly**.

Averages, Graphs and Speed

Turn back to page 5, and look again at the two car journeys shown at the top of the second column.

The brown car driving from Karachi to Lahore travels a distance of 200 km in 4 hours.

How many km does it travel in 1 hour?

We divide 200 km by 4 hours:

$$200 \div 4 = \frac{200}{4} = 50 \text{ km}$$

We say that the car is travelling at an **average speed** of **50 km per hour** or 50 km/hr.

Speed is the word we use for the **rate** at which we cover a certain unit of **distance** in a given unit of **time**. The average speed of a vehicle can be calculated by dividing the distance covered by the time taken.

For example, let us now look at the black car on page 5.

Ambling along Rawalpindi, it travels only 100 km in 4 hours. To find its average speed, we divide 100 by 4:

$$100 \div 4 = \frac{100}{4} = 25 \text{ km}$$

The black car is travelling at an average speed of 25 km/hr.

Remember: Distance, speed and time are the three things that matter when you are travelling...

4. Study the graphs, then work out the average speed for each journey.

★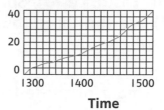

Distance (km)

Time

Average speed = 40 km ÷ 2 hours

= 20 km/hr

a. Distance (km)

b. Distance (km)

c. Distance (km)

5. Work out these average speeds.

★ 90 km covered in 2 hours

Average speed $= \frac{90}{2} = 45$ kmph

a. 105 km covered in 5 hours

b. 900 km covered in 3 hours

c. 448 km covered in 8 hours

OXFORD
UNIVERSITY PRESS

Distance, Speed and Time

·We have just seen that if we know the **distance** covered and the **time** taken, we can easily calculate the average **speed** of a journey.

As Sid puts it, Distance (D), Speed (S) and Time (T) are the three things that matter when you are travelling.

If you know **any 2** of those factors, you can work out the **third one**.

For example, if you know the distance (D) and the average speed (S), you can work out the time (T) a journey took:

Distance = 200 km
Speed = 40 km/hr (40 kmph)

$$\therefore \text{Time} = \frac{\text{Distance}}{\text{Speed}} = \frac{200}{40} = 5$$

Time = 5 hours

Suppose you know the time (T) a journey took and the average speed (S). How do you work out the distance (D)?

Simple!

Time = 6 hours
Speed = 35 km/hr (35 kmph)
$\therefore$ Distance = Time × Speed
= 6 × 35
= 210 km

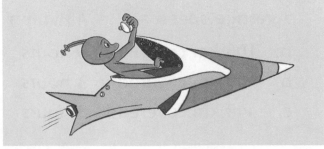

In a moment of genius, Sid has thought of the following diagram to show the relationship between Distance (D), Speed (S) and Time (T):

If you want the rule (formula) for **distance**, place your thumb over the 'D' to get:

$$D = S \times T$$

If you want the formula for **speed**, place your thumb over the 'S' to get:

$$S = \frac{D}{T}$$

If you cannot remember the formula for **time**, cover the 'T' to get:

$$T = \frac{D}{S}$$

1. Find the time taken for each journey.

   a. D = 100 km, S = 20 kmph,
   T= _____

   b. S = 55 kmph, D = 110 km,
   T = _____

   c. D = 540 km, S = 60 kmph,
   T = _____

2. Solve the following.

   a. A motorcycle averages 50 kmph. How long does it take to travel 25 km?

   b. How long will a bus travelling at an average speed of 45 kmph take to cover a distance of 225 km?

3. Work out the distance travelled in each of these journeys.

   a. S = 30 kmph, T = 5 hrs, D = ?

   b. S = 55 kmph, T = 4 hrs, D = ?

   c. T = $12\frac{1}{2}$ hrs, S = 50 kmph, D = ?

4. Work out the average speed of these journeys.

   a. T = 5 hrs, D = 360 km, S = ?

   b. T = 16 hrs, D = 1200 km, S = ?

   c. T = 7 hrs, D = 497 km, S = ?

5. Calculate values in the blanks.

   a. S = 40 kmph, T = ?, D = 480 km

   b. T = 5 hrs, D = 720 km, S = ?

   c. S = ?, T = 12 hrs, D = 732 km

   d. D = 1350 km, S = 50 kmph, T = ?

   e. S = 60 kmph, D = ?, T = $2\frac{1}{2}$ hrs

   f. D = ?, T = $4\frac{1}{2}$ hrs, S = 70 kmph

6. Copy and complete the table:

	Distance	Time	Speed
a.	240 km	6 hr	
b.		$\frac{1}{2}$ hr	40 kmph
c.	450 km		90 kmph
d.	1500 km	25 hrs	

7. Solve, making complete statements.

   a. If a cyclist travels 90 km in 5 hours, what is her average speed?

   b. Sprog Spacewalker takes part in a marathon race 18 km long. If his average speed is 6 kmph, how long does he take to complete the race?

   c. How far will a gas-filled balloon travel in 8 hours if its average speed is $10\frac{1}{2}$ kmph?

   d. How long will it take Sue Spacewalker to run 12 km at 8 kmph? If Selvi takes 2 hours to run the same distance, what is her average speed?

Thinking about Temperature

Let us think about the types of measurement we have learnt to use. We have learnt to measure:

- **money**, using rupees and paise as our units of measurement,
- **length**, **weight** and **capacity**, using measures based on the metric system,
- the **area** covered by an object and the **volume** of space it takes up,
- **time**, something we need to measure all through the day,
- **angles** and **bearings**.

But there are plenty of other things to be measured in the world around us. One of them is **temperature**.

We can tell then that something is very hot..

burger

...or very cold

ice cream

We can also recognize a very hot or unusually cold outside temperature. But sometimes we need to make an exact **measurement**. Reny, for example, is feeling feverish.

To find out exactly how high a fever he has, he uses a special instrument called a **thermometer**.

There is probably a thermometer in your school. Ask your teacher to show it to you.
It will look like this:

'Thermometer' simply means 'heat measuring instrument'. The most common type of thermometer is a glass tube with a very narrow inner tube or **bore**. A **bulb** at one end contains mercury or some other liquid. The mercury or other liquid also reaches a certain distance up the bore.

OXFORD
UNIVERSITY PRESS

All about Temperature

When the temperature **rises**, the liquid in the bulb **expands**, and is pushed up the narrow bore. When the temperature **falls**, the liquid **contracts** and is pushed back down the bore:

If you look carefully at a thermometer, you will see a series of tiny numbers marked along its glass tube.

These mark **degrees**, the unit of measurement for temperature. The symbol ° is used as a short way of writing the word 'degree'.

(A degree measures angles too!)

Temperature is measured on a range between two reference points:

  a. The **melting point of ice** (also known as the **freezing point of water**) and

  b. The **boiling point of water**.

Two different temperature scales are in common use today:

A. **The Fahrenheit** [say 'Farren-hite'] **scale**. This is named after a German scientist, G. Fahrenheit. It has the melting point of ice at 32 degrees (32°F) and the boiling point of water at 212 degrees (212°F). It is still much in use in Britain and the USA.

B. **The Celsius** [say 'Sell-si-us'] **scale**. This gets its name from Celsius, a Swedish astronomer. Its two reference points are 0°C and 100°C. It is used in many countries, including Pakistan, and is the scale used by the International scientific community.

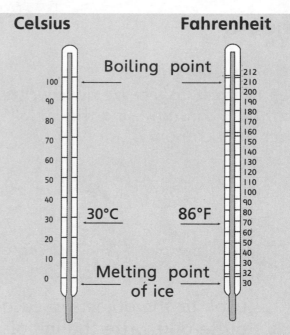

To convert Fahrenheit to Celsius:

First subtract 32, then multiply by $\frac{5}{9}$

Example: 59°F converted to Celsius

$=59-32=27;\quad \overset{3}{\cancel{27}}\times\frac{5}{\cancel{9}_1}=15°C$

To convert Celsius to Fahrenheit:

Multiply by $\frac{9}{5}$, then add 32:

Example: 30°C converted to Fahrenheit

$=\overset{6}{\cancel{30}}\times\frac{9}{\cancel{5}_1}=54+32=86°F$

 1. Convert these temperatures into the other scale (answer to 2 decimal places where necessary).

  a. 122°F   b. 45°C

  c. 77°F   d. 40°C

  e. 113°F   f. 35°C

145

Algebra

Use of Symbols

Look at these cages. We have written what they contain using the initial letter of each name:

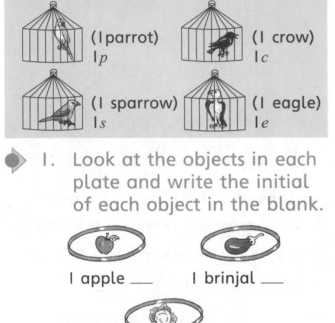

(1 parrot)
1 *p*

(1 crow)
1 *c*

(1 sparrow)
1 *s*

(1 eagle)
1 *e*

1. Look at the objects in each plate and write the initial of each object in the blank.

1 apple ___   1 brinjal ___

1 cauliflower ___

2. Now look at these boxes. Write the initial of each object.

A. (2 lollipops)   (3 sweets)

★ 1*l* + 1*l* or 2*l*

(2 chocolates)   (4 burgers)

___   ___

B. Now, write all these using different symbols of your choice. For example, 'lollipop' can be written as *w*, 'sweet' as *x* and so on.

___   ___

___   ___

C. If *x* stands for one rupee, write the amount of money each box contains, using *x*:

(Rupees seven)   (Rupees five)

___   ___

(Rupees ten)

___

D. Put all the money together, and write your answer using *x*:

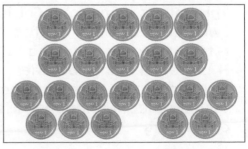

If we put all the items given on the previous page, in exercise 1 in one plate, we can write:

$$1a + 1b + 1c$$

This is an algebraic expression.

Look at the birds in this cage:

5 sparrows + 4 parrots + 2 eagles + 1 crow

We can use the initial letter of each word to write an algebraic expression:

$$5s + 4p + 2e + 1c$$

or, we can use any other letter, and write:

$$5d + 4r + 2w + 1o$$

1. Now, put all the items given in Exercise 2A, on the previous page, in one tray.

Write the contents of the tray, using the English letters.

2. Now, write each group as an algebraic expression, using first the initial letter and then the last letter of each word.

a. 2 apples + 3 bananas + 1 mango + 1 watermelon

b. 2 (pairs of) scissors, two knives, 3 forks and 1 teapot

OXFORD
UNIVERSITY PRESS

Addition and Subtraction of Algebraic Expressions

We often use different symbols in place of objects, to write terms which cannot be added together.

2 apples + 3 bananas + 1 mango + 1 watermelon may be written as

$$2w + 3x + 1y + 1z$$

(if we know that apple = w, banana = x, mango = y and watermelon = z)

1. Now, write the following sets of objects as algebraic expressions, using different letters of your choice.

   a. 5 books, 3 notebooks and 1 atlas.
   b. 3 ships, 1 boat and 2 kayaks.
   c. 4 ink pens, 3 ballpoint pens, 12 pencils and 1 felt-tip pen.

Look at these two baskets of vegetables. We put all the vegetables together, and write like this:

1 cauliflower
+ 2 brinjals
+ 4 tomatoes
+ 4 onions
     or $1c + 2b + 4t + 4o$

1 cauliflower
+ 3 brinjals
+ 5 onions
     or $1c + 3b + 5o$

On adding, we get $2c + 5b + 4t + 9o$

2. Now, add each set of the following expressions.

   a. $2x + 3y + 4z$; $5x + 2y + 4z$
   b. $2a + 3b + 4c + 1d$; $5a + 4b + 2c$
   c. $1p + 2q + 3r$; $2q + 3r$; $4p + 2q$

If 2 sparrows, 1 crow and 1 eagle fly away from the cage, how many birds are left?

We write:
   5 sparrows + 4 parrots +
   2 eagles + 1 crow
   or $5s + 4p + 2e + 1c$
   $2s + 1e + 1c$ (fly away)
   We are left with: $3s + 4p + 1e$

3. Take away.

   a. $2x + 3y$ from $5x + 8y$
   b. $3p + 2q + 1r$ from $5p + 2q + 3r + 3s$
   c. $2a + 1b + 1c$ from $2a + 1b + 1c + 1d$

We find the perimeters of equilateral triangles like this:

(triangle side: 2 cm)
Perimeter = 2 cm + 2 cm + 2cm
= 3 × 2 = 6 cm
(triangle side: 4 cm)
Perimeter = 4 cm + 4 cm + 4 cm
= 3 × 4 = 12 cm
(triangle side: a cm)
Perimeter = a cm + a cm + a cm
= 3 × a = 3a cm

1. Write in short.

★ $a + a + a + a + a = 5 \times a = 5a$

a. $x + x + x$

b. $y + y + y$

c. $f + f + f + f + f + f$

2. Now, find the perimeter of each of these figures.

a. Triangle with side x cm

b. Square with side y cm

c. Hexagon with side z cm

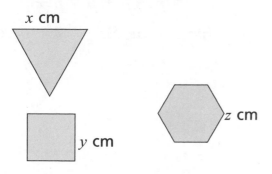

3. Write as an addition:

★ $6p = p + p + p + p + p + p$

a. $3g$ b. $5q$ c. $8z$

We write the expression for the sum of two like expressions like this:
(2 mangoes + 3 bananas) or
(2m + 3b)

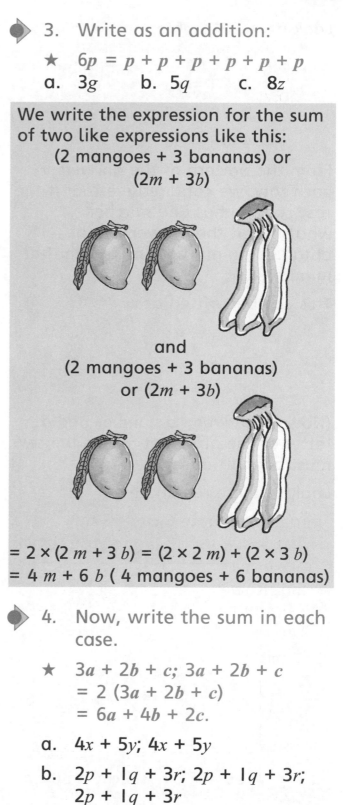

and
(2 mangoes + 3 bananas)
or (2m + 3b)

= 2 × (2 m + 3 b) = (2 × 2 m) + (2 × 3 b)
= 4 m + 6 b (4 mangoes + 6 bananas)

4. Now, write the sum in each case.

★ $3a + 2b + c$; $3a + 2b + c$
= 2 (3a + 2b + c)
= 6a + 4b + 2c.

a. $4x + 5y$; $4x + 5y$

b. $2p + 1q + 3r$; $2p + 1q + 3r$;
$2p + 1q + 3r$

OXFORD
UNIVERSITY PRESS

Multiplication of Unlike Terms

Look at the 9's table:

$$1 \times 9 = 9$$
$$2 \times 9 = 18$$
$$3 \times 9 = 27$$
$$4 \times 9 = 36$$

From the pattern of the answers in each row, we can presume that if the first column has any number whatsoever, the answer will be obtained by multiplying 9 with that number.

This can be written as

$$y \times 9 = 9y$$

or

$$p \times 9 = 9p$$

(No sign between a number and a letter of the alphabet means the two must be multiplied)

Look at these rectangles:

a. Rectangle 6 cm × 5 cm

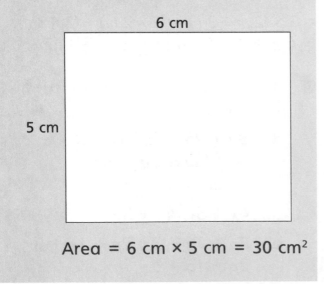

Area = 6 cm × 5 cm = 30 cm²

b. Rectangle 5 cm × 3 cm

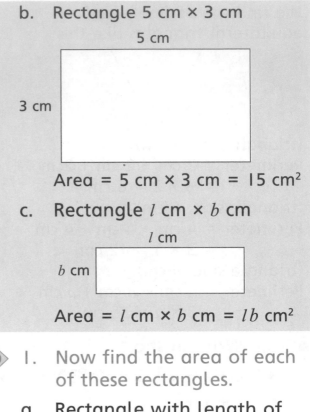

Area = 5 cm × 3 cm = 15 cm²

c. Rectangle l cm × b cm

l cm

b cm

Area = l cm × b cm = lb cm²

1. Now find the area of each of these rectangles.

a. Rectangle with length of p cm, and breadth q cm

b. Square with side s cm

c. Rectangle with length f cm and breadth g cm

2. Expand and write.

$$5p = 5 \times p \text{ (or } 5.p)$$
$$= p + p + p + p + p$$

a. $6m$ b. $9z$ c. pq cm²

Remember the following:

1. $x + x + x + x = 4x$

   $4x$ is a term, and 4 is the coefficient of x.

2. $2m$, $5m$, $6m$ are **like** terms, since m represents the same object in each case. You can add like terms.

   You can subtract one term from another term like it.

3. $2m$, $2o$ and $5n$ are **unlike** terms, since m, n and o represent different objects.

4. The sum of two unlike terms, x and y, is $x + y$.

5. The difference between x and y (if $x > y$) is $x - y$.

6. The product of x and y is xy.

7. $2p + 4q$ is an algebraic expression.

8. To add two expressions, like terms must be added together.

For example, the sum of $(2a + 3b)$ and $(3b + 4a)$ is:

$$\begin{array}{r} (2a + 3b) \\ + \ (4a + 3b) \\ \hline 6a + 6b \end{array}$$

9. To subtract one expression from another, you must find the difference of like terms.

For example, the difference between $(4x + 5y)$ and $(2y + 3x)$ is:

$$\begin{array}{r} (4x + 5y) \\ - \ (3x + 2y) \\ \hline 1x + 3y \end{array}$$

10. To multiply an expression by a given number, each term must be separately multiplied by that number.

For example,

$(3x + 2y) + (3x + 2y)$

$= 2 \times (3x + 2y)$

$= 6x + 4y$

Exercise

Write out these problems in algebraic terms and work them out.

1. If one pineapple costs Rs 10, find the cost of:

   a 5 pineapples

   b. 3 pineapples

   c. x pineapples

OXFORD
UNIVERSITY PRESS

2. Two bags contain 3 lollipops and 4 sweets each. Write the sum as an algebraic expression.

3. One cage has 2 parrots and 3 sparrows, and the other has 1 parrot, 1 crow and 1 sparrow. Birds from these two cages are put together in a larger cage. Write the sum as an algebraic expression.

4. There were 4 sweets in a box; two were eaten by Adil. Write this as an algebraic term.

5. There were 4 cakes and 4 sandwiches on a plate. Rabia ate one of each. Write this as an algebraic expression.

6. Work these out:

   a. $p + p + p + p + p + p =$ _____

   b. $4k =$ _____

   c. $3d - 2d =$ _____

   d. $7x + 3x + 2x =$ _____

   e. $8c - 2c =$ _____

7. Add:

   a. $(3a + 4b) + (5b + 4a + 2c)$

   b. $(2x + 3y) + (5y + 2y)$

8. Subtract:

   a. $(3x + 4y) - (2y + 1x)$

   b. $(9p + 8r) - (4r + 3p)$

9. Multiply:

   a. $a \times b$ b. $p \times r$ c. $y \times z$

REVIEW OF THE YEAR

1. Place in Pakistani periods and write the number name.
    a. 5672318   b. 74028301
    c. 6009053   d. 90755620

2. Change into International periods and write the International number name.
    a. 42,03,721   b. 3,16,72,049
    c. 50,47,834   d. 8,02,46,118

3. Write the value of the coloured digit.
    a. 1,627,148   b. 7,24,16,831
    c. 22,14,690   d. 84,172,063

4. For each number, write (i) the predecessor and (ii) the successor.
    a. 2,348,000   b. 6,10,00,000
    c. 14,17,600   d. 84,000,000

5. Write vertically and complete.
    a. 1,40,732 + 8,64,395 +28
    b. 7,640,117 − 4,584,623
    c. 18,96,23,141 + 3292 + 764
    d. 1468.29 − 979.54

6. Round off each number (i) to the nearest 10 and; (ii) to the nearest 100.
    a. 643   b. 82,555   c. 1,29,387

7. Round off each number (i) to 1 decimal place and (ii) to 2 decimal places.
    a. 2.461   b. 84.099
    c. 6.191   d. 100.335

8. Write vertically and complete.
    a. 1629 × 312   b. 8.197 × 36
    c. 8074 × 593   d. 10.895 × 75

9. Solve, writing your answer to two decimal places where necessary.
    a. 97,920 ÷ 384
    b. 69,482 ÷ 77
    c. 46,839 ÷ 47
    d. 108,964 ÷ 98

10. Prepare bills for these customers.
    a. **Hungry Crocodile**: 20 kg of rice at Rs 3.75/kg; $16\frac{3}{4}$ kg of fish at Rs 24/kg; 5 l of cooking oil at Rs 18.50/l; 10 packets of biscuits at Rs 11.35/packet.

    b. **Adil**: 12 kg of wheat flour at Rs 4.15/kg; 5.5 kg of sugar at Rs 6.25/kg; 2.5 l of cream at Rs 18.60/l; 25 chocolate bars at Rs 9.85 each.

OXFORD
UNIVERSITY PRESS

11. Simplify.
    a. 6 × 5 + 18 − 4
    b. 4 + 18 ÷ 3 × 24
    c. 9 × 21 ÷ 7 + 14 − 5
    d. 8.4 × 0.16 − 0.614

12. Simplify.
    a. (0.38 × 4.62) + 10.95
    b. 4.61 + {2.41 + (3.82 − 1.75)}
    c. $3\frac{5}{6} + \left\{1\frac{1}{6} + \left(\frac{1}{3} \times \frac{3}{4}\right)\right\}$
    d. [{84 − (21 + 3)} ÷ 12] + 74
    e. {31 − (16.3 + 8.6)} × 1000

13. Work out the areas.

    a.
    5 m
    7 m

    b.
    2 m
    7 m
    3 m
    5.5 m

    c.
    4.5 m
    4 m

    d.
    6 m
    5 m

14. Work out the volume of these cuboids (in cm³ or m³):
    a. $l = 4.2\,cm$, $b = 5\,cm$, $h = 1.5\,cm$
    b. $l = 10\,m$, $b = 3.5\,m$, $h = 4.3\,m$
    c. $l = 6.9\,cm$, $b = 7.5\,cm$, $h = 2.2\,cm$

15. Write down:
    a. any 5-digit number divisible by 4.
    b. any 6-digit number divisible by 8.
    c. any numbers from this list which are divisible by 15:
        400, 7020, 11,620, 15,055.

16. Write the numbers whose prime factors are given here, using brackets to help you.
    a. 2 × 2 × 2 × 3
    b. 2 × 2 × 2 × 5 × 5
    c. 2 × 3 × 5 × 7 × 7 × 11

17. Using prime factorization, find the HCF of:
    a. 56 and 140
    b. 63 and 54

18. Find the HCF, using the long division method.
    a. 1026; 247   b. 2146; 1184
    c. 368; 1173   d. 1377; 1836

19. Find the LCM of each set.
    a. 12, 15, 21   b. 24, 32, 26
    c. 10, 12, 18   d. 27, 30, 15

20. Fill in the blanks.

   a. If the product of 2 numbers is 270 and their HCF is 3, their LCM is _____.

   b. For a pair of numbers, the HCF is 4 and the LCM is 252. If one of the numbers is 28, the other number is _____.

21. Solve, giving each answer in its lowest terms.

   a. $\dfrac{2}{9} \times \dfrac{2}{3}$ b. $5\dfrac{3}{7} \times 6\dfrac{4}{5}$

   c. $3\dfrac{7}{8} \div 2$ d. $\dfrac{1}{3} \times \dfrac{1}{6} \times \dfrac{2}{5}$

   e. $9\dfrac{2}{3} \div 1\dfrac{5}{6}$ f. $\dfrac{1}{5} \div \dfrac{3}{10}$

22. Multiply each number (i) by 10, (ii) by 100 and (iii) by 1000.

   a. 4.8   b. 1.47

   c. 6.87   d. 4.535

23. Solve.

   a. 0.6 × 0.4   b. 3.091 × 4.5

   c. 0.63 ÷ 0.21 d. 1.752 ÷ 0.219

   e. 2.81 × 3.6   f. 0.12 ÷ 0.006

24. Write denominators in place of ∗s, then complete the sums.

   a. $2.34 \times 4.61 = \dfrac{107874}{*}$

   b. $3.604 \times 7.3 = \dfrac{263092}{*}$

25. Change these into decimals, giving your answer (i) to 2 decimal places and (ii) to 3 decimal places.

   a. $\dfrac{5}{11}$ b. $\dfrac{9}{13}$ c. $\dfrac{40}{6}$

26. Write as percentages, using the % symbol.

   a. $\dfrac{14}{25}$ b. $\dfrac{3}{20}$ c. $3\dfrac{2}{5}$

27. Write as percentages (to 2 decimal places where necessary).

   a. $1\dfrac{2}{3}$ b. $4\dfrac{1}{9}$ c. $3\dfrac{5}{6}$

28. Change into fractions or mixed numbers, reducing where you can.

   a. 80%   b. 224%   c. 16%

   d. 75%   e. 155%   f. 44%

29. Change into decimals.

   a. 45%   b. 672%   c. 12%

   d. 55%   e. 752%   f. 34%

30. Change into percentages.

   a. 0.018   b. 1.64   c. 0.143

OXFORD
UNIVERSITY PRESS

31. Calculate.

    a. 20% of Rs 40.75

    b. The percentage profit where C.P. = Rs 800 and S.P. = Rs 950

    c. 70% of 5600 l of water

    d. The percentage profit where S.P. = Rs 5000 and C.P. = Rs 3800 (to 3 decimal places)

32. Calculate the interest where:

    a. P = Rs 1200, R = 5%, T = 3 years

    b. P = Rs 5000, R = $6\frac{1}{2}$%, T = 4 years

    c. P = Rs 850, R = $9\frac{1}{2}$%, T = 2 years

33. Construct these, using the appropriate instrument.

    a. Reflex ∠ABC = 240°

    b. A circle of diameter 7.8 cm

    c. A circle of radius 6.0 cm with arc PQR marked on it.

34. Complete these statements.

    a. If each side of △ABC is 4.5 cm, ∠ABC = _____ degrees.

    b. If two angles of an isosceles △PQR are 50° each, the third angle = _____°.

    c. If a △ has angles of 30°, 45°, and 105°, it is a _____ △.

    d. If a coral reef is due West of the Golden Cockroach, its bearing = _____°.

35. Construct triangles to match these dimensions.

	AB	BC	AC	∠BAC	∠ABC
a.	4 cm	5 cm	3.5 cm	-	-
b.	6 cm	-	4 cm	55°	-
c.	5 cm	7 cm	-	-	80°
d.	7.5 cm	-	-	35°	45°

36. Construct:

    a. Parallel lines AB and CD, each 3.2 cm long and 2.0 cm apart.

    b. Two concentric circles, one of radius 3.5 cm and the other of radius 4.4 cm.

    c. Line PQ perpendicular to the end point of line ST.

37. Solve, making complete statements.

    a. Over a 3-month period, Kashif's monthly income from weaving handloom cloth was Rs 1460, Rs 2900 and Rs 3741. What was his average income for the period?

    b. If a rickshaw averages 30 kmph, how long will it take to cover 50 km?

WORKSHEET 1

Fun with Numbers

Each question is followed by four answers, only one of which is correct. Choose the correct answer and underline it.

1. What is the value of the digit 6 in 60,594?

    a. 6000   b.   60,000

    c. 600   d.   6,00,000

2. Ten lakh is the same as

    a. 5 million   b. 10 million

    c. 10 thousand   d. 1 million

3. The sum of the place value of 6 in the numeral 6,46,060 is

    a. 6,06,060   b.   6,60,000

    c. 6,60,600   d.   6,00,000

4. The product of 840 and 1000 is

    a. 8,4.20,000   b.   84,000

    c. 8,40,000   d.   8400

5. The predecessor of 9,07,000 is

    a. 9,07,600   b.   9,06,000

    c. 9,06,999   d.   9,07,199

6. 9999 + 999 = _____

    a. 10,000   b.   10,999

    c. 10,900   d.   10,998

7. If 9 pens cost Rs 135, what will the cost of one pen be?

    a. Rs 6   b.   Rs 9.50

    c. Rs 11.20   d.   Rs 15

8. The greatest 6-digit number that can be formed using the digits 2, 0, 1, 5, 7, 8 is

    a. 1,05,782   b.   8,75,210

    c. 8,57,210   d.   8,72,510

9. Which number should replace the question mark?

    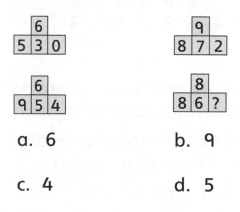

    a. 6   b. 9

    c. 4   d. 5

OXFORD
UNIVERSITY PRESS

7-Digit Numbers

1. Put the correct sign (>, < or =) in the box.

    a. 84,04,567 ☐ 84,04,657

    b. 6,005,426 ☐ 6,005,246

    c. 81,94,250 ☐ 8,194,250

2. Write your answer in words.

    a. 100 more than 9,99,999

    b. 1000 more than 1,890,999

    c. The successor of 26,17,599

3. Add these numbers.

    ```
        1 0 1 1 0 0
        2 5 6 0 3 1
        4 8 5 9 2 1
    +   6 3 1 1 5 9
    ```

    a. Write the total according to the International system.

    b. Write the total according to the Pakistani system.

    c. Write the total in words according to the Pakistani system.

4. Add the smallest 7-digit number to the greatest 5-digit number. Write your answer in words.

5. What is the difference between the place-value of the 2s in 8,234,260?

6. Complete this table.

	INTERNATIONAL	PAKISTANI
a.	3,462,054	
b.		72,58,900
c.		10,50,000
d.	7,490,100	

7. State whether the following statements are True or False.

    a. Seven lakh is the same as seventy thousand.
    b. One million is the same as ten lakh.
    c. A million is more than a billion.

8. How many seconds has a 9-year-old boy lived?

WORKSHEET 3

Area and Perimeter

Each question is followed by four answers, only one of which is correct. Choose the correct answer and underline it.

1. What is the area of the given figure?

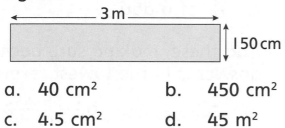

3 m

150 cm

   a. 40 cm²   b. 450 cm²
   c. 4.5 cm²   d. 45 m²

2. What is the total area of the two mats shown?

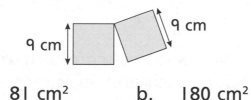

9 cm

9 cm

   a. 81 cm²   b. 180 cm²
   c. 162 cm²   d. 64 cm²

3. The area of a square is 49 cm². What is its perimeter?

   a. 14 cm²   b. 28 cm
   c. 280 cm   d. 490 cm²

4. The perimeter of a rectangular field whose length is 200 m and breadth is 180 m.

   a. 760 m   b. 7600 m
   c. 76 cm²   d. 760 cm²

5. Work out the following in your notebook.

   a. The length and breadth of a rectangular field are 12 m and 8 m respectively. What is the area of 3 such fields?

   b. A square garden has to be paved with bricks all around. Find the perimeter of the garden if the length of one side is 6.5 m.

   c. What is the area of the triangle shown?

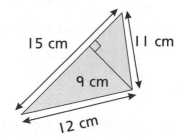

15 cm

11 cm

9 cm

12 cm

   d. The following figure is a sketch of a field. What is the perimeter of the field (i) in km and (ii) in m.

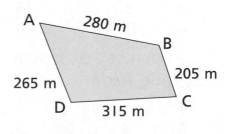

A   280 m   B

265 m   205 m

D   315 m   C

Can the length of BD be
(i)   more than 545?
(ii) less than 515?

OXFORD
UNIVERSITY PRESS

Fractions

1. Rewrite these fractions in their lowest terms.

   a. $\dfrac{16}{20}$ b. $\dfrac{125}{500}$ c. $\dfrac{15}{135}$

2. Rewrite these mixed numbers as improper fractions.

   a. $3\dfrac{1}{2}$ b. $6\dfrac{9}{12}$ c. $15\dfrac{2}{5}$

3. Rewrite these improper fractions as mixed numbers.

   a. $\dfrac{17}{8}$ b. $\dfrac{53}{9}$ c. $\dfrac{35}{6}$

4. Reduce the given fractions to their lowest terms.

   a. $\dfrac{28}{24}$ b. $\dfrac{140}{280}$ c. $\dfrac{13}{104}$

5. Compare the fractions and put the correct sign (>, < or =) in the blank.

   a. $\dfrac{1}{4}$ ___ $\dfrac{3}{20}$ b. $\dfrac{1}{5}$ ___ $\dfrac{2}{15}$

   c. $\dfrac{3}{4}$ ___ $\dfrac{3}{16}$ d. $\dfrac{16}{20}$ ___ $\dfrac{4}{5}$

6. Write each set of fractions in ascending order.

   a. $\dfrac{1}{6}$ $\dfrac{1}{4}$ $\dfrac{1}{20}$

   b. $\dfrac{1}{2}$ $\dfrac{3}{4}$ $\dfrac{5}{12}$

7. Write the answer.

   a. $\dfrac{1}{2}$ m = _____ cm

   b. $\dfrac{1}{5}$ of an hour _____

   c. $\dfrac{1}{6}$ of a day _____

8. Add these, making sure each answer is in the lowest terms.

   a. $\dfrac{2}{3} + \dfrac{7}{8}$ b. $3\dfrac{5}{16} + 2\dfrac{3}{8}$

   c. $\dfrac{8}{9} + \dfrac{5}{6}$ d. $4\dfrac{2}{3} + 1\dfrac{7}{8}$

   e. $1\dfrac{1}{3} + 2\dfrac{1}{6}$

9. Now subtract carefully, making sure each answer is in its lowest terms.

   a. $\dfrac{8}{15} - \dfrac{1}{5}$ b. $8\dfrac{3}{16} - 4\dfrac{5}{8}$

   c. $\dfrac{9}{10} - \dfrac{3}{4}$ d. $2\dfrac{7}{8} - 1\dfrac{11}{24}$

   e. $4\dfrac{1}{3} - 2\dfrac{5}{12}$

Numbers can be fun

Each question is followed by four answers, only one of which is correct. Choose the correct answer and underline it.

1. $99 \div 11$ has the same value as:
   a. $(2 + 3) + 4$
   b. $3 \times (3 \times 2)$
   c. $99 \div 10 + 1$
   d. $11 - 2 \times 0$

2. What is $1\frac{4}{5} \times \frac{2}{3}$?
   a. $1\frac{1}{5}$
   b. $1\frac{4}{5}$
   c. $\frac{8}{15}$
   d. $1\frac{8}{15}$

3. 8649 rounded off to the nearest 100 is
   a. 8600
   b. 8650
   c. 8610
   d. 8700

4. 13.8×10 is the same as
   a. 138
   b. 1380
   c. 13800
   d. 138.5

5. The prime number after 19 is
   a. 21
   b. 24
   c. 23
   d. 29

6. What will the cost of 70 cans of cola be, when one costs Rs 7.70?
   a. Rs 539.00
   b. Rs 5390
   c. Rs 593
   d. Rs 5390.50

7. Which of these is divisible by 4?
   a. 1650
   b. 2832
   c. 1718
   d. 3910

8. What is the value of 55.899 when rounded off to 2 decimal places?
   a. 55.90
   b. 56
   c. 55.00
   d. 55.80

WORKSHEET 6

Mathematical Teasers

1. The Calculating Cook

If it takes 3 minutes to boil an egg, how long will it take to boil 6 eggs?

2. Square Geometry

In this arrangement there are ten matchsticks forming three squares. Which two must be removed to obtain two squares?

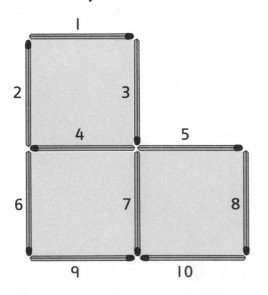

3. The Lazy Dog

Two dogs are balanced on a rope which goes over a pulley. The lazy dog remains stationary, while the other one climbs up the rope. What happens to the lazy dog?

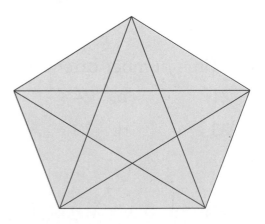

4. A Long Count

How many triangles are there in this figure?

Quiz Time

1. Fill in the blanks.

    a. A seven-sided polygon is called a _____ .

    b. The supplement of 29° is _____ .

    c. The complement of 43° is _____ .

    d. _____ lines can be drawn from one point.

    e. We need _____ points to draw a triangle.

    f. A ray has only _____ end point.

    g. The area of a triangle is $\frac{1}{2}$ _____ .

    h. A circle can have _____ semicircles.

2. Write True or False.

    a. A circle is a closed figure.

    b. A diameter is the longest chord in a circle.

    c. A circle can have many chords.

    d. A triangle can have only one obtuse angle.

    e. The sum of the angles in a rectangle is 360 °.

3. You will need a compass. Put the compass point on the dots and draw circles. Each circle you draw must pass exactly through Y.

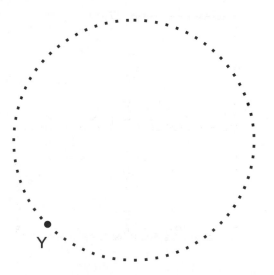

OXFORD
UNIVERSITY PRESS

WORKSHEET 8

Geometry

1. Find the missing angles in these triangles.

   a.
   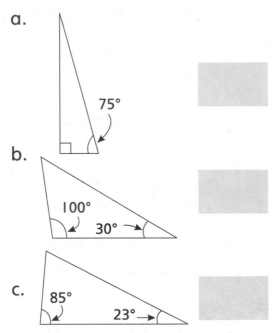
   75°

   b.
   100° 30°

   c.
   85° 23°

2. Find the angle at each point.

   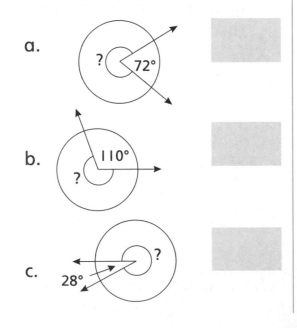

   a.
   ? 72°

   b.
   110° ?

   c.
   28° ?

3. Estimate the size of these angles. Then label them acute, reflex, obtuse, or right.

   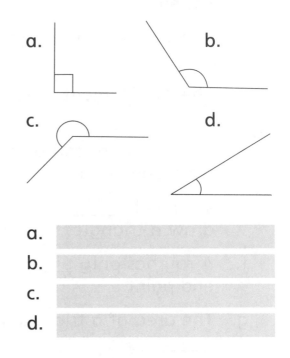

   a.   b.

   c.   d.

   a. _____
   b. _____
   c. _____
   d. _____

4. Draw an angle of 85° to the nearest degree. Mark it acute or obtuse.

5. Measure this acute angle to the nearest degree. Then measure the reflex angle too.

   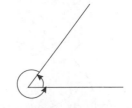

   What do you find?

MATHS LAB
ACTIVITY 1

Objective: To study factorization of prime and composite numbers

Materials required:

1. Cardboards cut out in circular shapes with numbers, prime or composite, written in the centre. For example, 2, 6, 7, 12, 13, 16, 50, 75, 100 and so on.

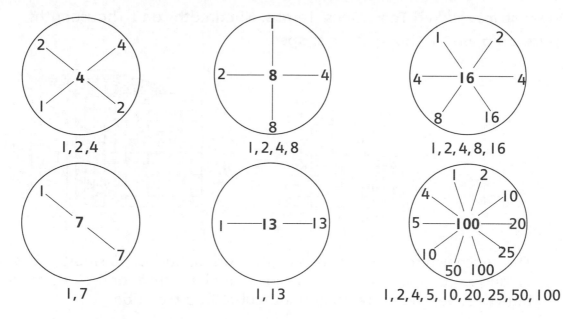

1, 2, 4   1, 2, 4, 8   1, 2, 4, 8, 16

1, 7   1, 13   1, 2, 4, 5, 10, 20, 25, 50, 100

Steps:

1. The teacher writes some numbers on the board and discusses the definitions of prime numbers and composite numbers.

2. The students are then asked to go up to the board one-by-one and identify the numbers that are prime and those that are not.

3. The teacher calls a student and asks him/her to draw a circle on the board and write any number in the centre of the circle.

4. Then another student is asked to write the factors of the number near the circumference of the circle as shown above.

5. Now, the class is divided into groups of four and each group is handed a cardboard disc. Each group needs to work out the factors of at least 4 numbers. When all have finished, the groups exchange their factor-wheels and correct each other's work.

● **Teacher's Note:** Let the students know that the number 1 was not a part of the discussion because 1 is neither prime nor composite. It has only 1 factor. All prime numbers have 2 factors while all composite numbers have 3 or more factors.

OXFORD
UNIVERSITY PRESS

Objective: To introduce decimals to children

Materials required:

1. Wooden cubes, square rods and slabs of various sizes, each with a metallic ring screwed on one side to hang it from.

2. Paper strips marked Tens, Ones, Tenths, Hundredths and Thousandths.

3. Space on a wall to hang these shapes.

Steps:

1. The teacher discusses the sizes of the various solids. 10 small cubes are arranged to make one rod, 10 rods to make a slab, and 10 slabs to make a big cube. So, there are 1000 small cubes in a big cube.

2. The teacher then discusses $\frac{1}{10}$th, $\frac{1}{100}$th and $\frac{1}{1000}$th of a whole. This is followed up with the teacher displaying the big cube and its decimal fractions to the children.

3. She explains that the big cube is the ones cube (or a whole cube).

4. One of the students is asked to place the ones cube against the wall. One more student comes up and hangs the strip with 'ones' written on it, above the big cube.

5. Then, another student puts the slab on the hook in the 'tenths' column, the rod in the 'hundredths' column and the small cube in the 'thousandths' column.

• **Teacher's Note:** The concept of decimals can be taught with squares cut out from sheets of a notebook. It is worth taking the trouble to explain the decimal system properly so that the child never has any problems dealing with decimal fractions. This conversion rod is very useful for teaching conversion of grams into kilograms, or centimetres into metres.

Objective: To learn simple facts of addition and subtraction

Materials required:

1. Wall charts displaying:
   a. 1 to 100 Number Square (Square of 10)   c. 1 to 81 Number Square (Square of 9)
   b. 1 to 64 Number Square (Square of 8)   d. 1 to 49 Number Square (Square of 7)
2. Several number crosses to fit the above number squares, all kept face down in a box.

Steps:

1. The teacher asks a student to take out a number cross and show it to the class. The rest of the children help the student decide which number square it will fit into.

2. The teacher explains that this can be found by calculating the difference of any two consecutive numbers, vertically. She explains this with the help of 3 examples.

6	52	49
13 14 15	60 61 62	58 59 60
22	70	69

$22 - 14 = 14 - 6 = 8$ $70 - 61 = 61 - 52 = 9$ $69 - 59 = 59 - 49 = 10$
(Square of 8)   **(Square of 9)**   **(Square of 10)**

3. Different students are then asked to pick up number crosses from the box and place them on the correct number square.

4. The teacher points out that the three vertical numbers in any number cross always have the same sum as the three horizontal numbers.

   For example, in the first two number crosses given above:

   $13 + 14 + 15 = 6 + 14 + 22 = 42$. Also, $3 \times 14 = 42$

   $52 + 61 + 70 = 60 + 61 + 62 = 183$. Also, $3 \times 61 = 183$

5. The children then carry out these calculations with different number crosses.

- **Teacher's Note:** When the number of terms in a number series is odd and the difference between any two consecutive numbers is the same, then the sum of the series can be found by multiplying the number in the centre by the total numbers in the series.
  For example, in the series: 42 53 64 75 86 (difference between two consecutive numbers = 11),
  $42 + 53 + 64 + 75 + 86 = 320 = 5$ (numbers in the series) $\times 64$ (number in the centre)
  Similarly, in the series 30, 40, 50, 60, 70, 80, 90, 100, 110:
  $30 + 40 + 50 + 60 + 70 + 80 + 90 + 100 + 110 = 9 \times 70 = 630$
  When the number of terms is even, such as $9 + 11 + 13 + 15 + 17 + 19$, remove either the first or the last number, find the sum as mentioned above, and add the sum to the removed number,
  i.e. $11 + 13 + 15 + 17 + 19 = 5 \times 15 = 75$, and $75 + 9 = 84$. So, the sum of the series is 84.

Objective: To make a permanent calendar

Materials required:

1. One rectangular cardboard of any convenient size for all the students in the class with numbers written on it as shown below and another larger one for the teacher.

						1	2	3	4	5	6	7
2	3	4	5	6	7	8	9	10	11	12	13	14
9	10	11	12	13	14	15	16	17	18	19	20	21
16	17	18	19	20	21	22	23	24	25	26	27	23
23	24	25	26	27	28	29	30	31				
30	31											

2. One more cardboard of the same size with holes punched in it to fit over the above cardboard (or transparent sheets can be printed with circles or boxes of the same size). A larger one for the teacher should also be made.

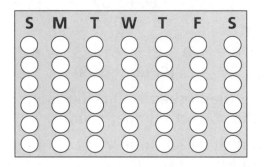

Steps:

1. The teacher picks up one cardboard of each type and puts the punched cardboard on top of the numbered one.

2. One of the students is called and asked to show the date of the day, using the two rectangles.

3. Suppose the date is 19th and it is a Wednesday. The student shows this by placing the 3rd hole in the middle column of the punched card on top of the number 19. The numbers show through the transparency sheet or holes.

4. Other students are also asked to check out different dates of different months in the same way. Once the day and the date is matched, all the days of a month fall into the required pattern.

• **Teacher's Note:** You may ask one of the students to write a row of numbers from the rectangle on the board. Then, ask another student to write the second row of numbers without looking at the calendar. Tell them to remember that the number below a given number in a calendar is 7 more than the number itself.

Objective: To calculate the perimeter of different shapes and make different patterns with these shapes

Materials required:

1. Various geometrical shapes, as shown, with some having such dimensions that they can fit together.
2. Pencil, rubber, sharpener, ruler.

Steps:

1. Children work in groups of four.
2. Each group is given different geometrical shapes made of plastic or cardboard.
3. The teacher then draws a grid on the board (a suitable grid for the board would contain squares of length 5 cm or 10 cm).

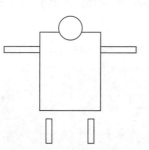
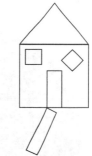

4. One of the students comes to the board, places his/her geometrical shape on the grid and counts around the edges.
5. Another student with a similar shape may then be asked to join this student and count round the edges of the combined shape.
6. Then, another pair of children may hold different shapes together and try to make different patterns.
7. The rest of the children work at their desks, putting together different shapes to form various patterns.

- **Teacher's Note:** At a later stage, ask the children to find combined perimeter of these patterns and measure the circumference of circular shapes using a cord. Also, help them in drawing more complex tessellations (tiling patterns).

OXFORD
UNIVERSITY PRESS

Book **Piracy** and **Plagiarism** are **Crimes.**
Beware of both!

Look out for the new security label whenever you purchase an Oxford textbook or supplementary reader. Labels with the features shown below are proof of genuine Oxford books.

- An iridescent circle with OUP written on it is featured on the left side of the label. The circle changes colour from orange to green when viewed from different angles.

- The labels tear if peeled from the book cover.

- The labels have security cut marks on the right and the left side to prevent them from being peeled off and reused.

- The word 'ORIGINAL' appears when the area under 'SCRATCH HERE' is rubbed with a coin.

- The words 'GENUINE' written in very small print become visible when viewed under a magnifying glass.

Do not accept the book if the label is missing, has been torn or tampered with, the colour on the security label does not change or the word 'ORIGINAL' does not appear upon rubbing the area with a coin.

Pirated books can be recognized by:

- inferior production quality
- low-grade paper
- variations in texture and colour
- poor print quality
- blurred text and images
- poor binding and trimming
- substandard appearance of the book

OXFORD
UNIVERSITY PRESS

If you suspect that you are being sold a pirated book without the security label, please contact:

Oxford University Press, No. 38, Sector 15, Korangi Industrial Area, P.O. Box No. 8214, Karachi-74900, Pakistan.
Tel.: (92-21) 35071580-86 • Fax: (92-21) 35055071-72 • E-mail: central.marketing.pk@oup.com
Website: www.oup.com/pk • Find us on